XAVIERA HOLLANDER HAS HOOKED THE NATION!

The controversial author of two of the fastest-selling
paperbacks in recent history is back again—with sensational new adventures and the wildest, most bizarre
collection of letters ever published.

★ Letters from readers with strange erotic tastes and
   even stranger ways of satisfying them
★ Letters from men and women who want to become
   prostitutes themselves
★ Letters so kinky they even made Xaviera blush
★ Letters so funny you'll fall out of bed laughing
★ Letters that are surprisingly tender and kind
★ Letters from professional virgins
★ Letters from would-be lesbians
★ Letters that run the wild, weird gamut of human
   emotions and experience

XAVIERA SCORES AGAIN....
with "LETTERS TO THE HAPPY HOOKER"!

D1462702

Letters To The Happy Hooker

Personally Selected by
Xaviera Hollander

Edited by Bob Abel & Michael Valenti

WARNER
PAPERBACK
LIBRARY

A Warner Communications Company

WARNER PAPERBACK LIBRARY EDITION
First Printing: August, 1973

Cover photo by Neal Slavin

Warner Paperback Library is a division of Warner Books, Inc.,
315 Park Avenue South, New York, N.Y. 10010.

 A Warner Communications Company

"Morality in sexual relations, when it is free from superstition, consists essentially of respect for the other person, and unwillingness to use that person solely as a means of personal gratification, without regard to his or her desires."

—BERTRAND RUSSELL, *Marriage and Morals XI*

"Sex is the most fun you can have without laughing."

—COMEDIAN JOEY ADAMS

"Every woman is a science."

—JOHN DONNE

SELECTED TABLE OF CONTENTS

A LETTER FROM XAVIERA

TORONTO, April 1973—I have been living in this lovely city, off and on, for most of the last nine months. I hope to remain here for the foreseeable future and perhaps make it my permanent home.

For the past few months I have been reviewing the several thousand letters I've received—first, as a result of *The Happy Hooker,* and more recently, a whole new avalanche of mail descending upon my publisher following the appearance of *Xaviera!* And I've just finished making my last selection of letters—I'm sure I've chosen far, far too many—from which my editors, Bob Abel and Mike Valenti, are going to edit this book, which is going to consist of well over 200 of the most interesting letters plus four of my more recent "adventures."

Truth to tell, I've enjoyed almost all the letters, except the truly nasty ones—and Bob and Mike and I have decided to leave some choice specimens in the book because they were, after all, a very real part of the letters I've received—and the ones from sick or very, very disturbed people. The harsh letters made me a little sad, but why should I be immune to criticism? But the real sickies genuinely distressed me, although I'm leaving to my editors the choice of how many of these letters to include. I trust their professionalism—just as, ahem, once upon a time I considered myself a top professional in my field. . . !

My next book will be a torrid travelogue of my wild-wilder-wildest "adventures" in Europe and Mexico and some other hot spots. NATO survived me, but not by much. On the other hand, I did manage to establish some important (if not lasting) new European alliances.

So unless you're allergic to spice, try it—you'll like it!

All my love,
Xaviera

P.S. My thanks again, as stated in the dedication to this book, to you, Dear Reader, for writing me and making this book happen. In all truth, it is your book.

INTRODUCTION

"The only kind of letters a woman likes to receive from a man are those which should not have been written."

—ANONYMOUS

"Not so, Anonymous!"

—X. HOLLANDER

RECEIVED, from Ms. Xaviera Hollander, over a period of the first three months of this year, several cartons of letters. The postal marks on these were from city, town and hamlet, from every American state and province of Canada. There were also some letters from Europe but not too many, since **The Happy Hooker** has been published in only a few European countries, and presumably those foreign language publishers got the bulk of mail to her.

A good many of the letters were typewritten, but the majority were in longhand. The age range, from the youngest correspondent to the eldest, was remarkable —probably six decades. And not a few of the senior citizens writing were anxious to enjoy some Medicare from Xaviera. Or was it Medicaid?

However, what is most assuredly the remarkable thing about the letters is the extraordinary range of emotions—the entire spectrum of human behavior— they express. It came as no surprise that there exists a vast subterranean sex life in America, but what is perhaps more revealing about Americans and Canadians in these letters is that sex seems to rank just behind meat prices in many people's lives. Thus **The Happy Hooker** and, later, **Xaviera!**, seemed to strike quite a responsive chord in readers' hearts and heads. (There were more visceral concerns as well.) All in all, therefore, the letters constitute a truly unique document which is a damn sight more exciting to read—and more fun, too —than collections of letters to Spiro or letters from camp (come to think of it, those could be the same letters). Anyone who can't find a few dozen surprises here is either a genuinely rotten person or else works for the FBI branch of the Post Office.

To be sure a number of the letters were from ardent Xavieraphiles but there were harsh or scolding letters as well. And the subject of prostitution is hardly one on which people are not tendentious—to paraphrase an old Midwestern expression: Does it really take a heap of humpin to make a 'house' a home?

Some letters were, well, kind of funky and others were disarmingly appealing. Some were religious, in the true sense of the word, while others were simply antagonistic toward Xaviera because they are against Original Sin. You'd think that Xaviera handed out the first apple. . . .

Lots and lots of people have sexual hangups. (No, Madam your husband cannot bring you to orgasm ten times a day.) But a new wave of sexual freedom is evident in the land. (Yes, Young Lady, it is healthy to be horny.) And hope springs eternal. (Sorry, Sir, but we really don't know if there is sex after death.)

There were a surprising sprinkling of would-be studs in the crowd and not a few crypto-lesbians. Plus hookers of both sexes. Plus kooks of both sexes. Plus clowns. Lots of clowns. As Kurt Vonnegut, Jr. says, Welcome to the Monkey House.

Our own favorite letters were the poignant ones, from people who had something sensitive or tender to say, and whose letters are a vote for the human condition. Then, too, there are some letters which still break us up at the fourth or fifth rereading of them. The last letter in the book is from one of these unconsciously funny correspondents. (Don't peek, dammit, the entire book has a rhythm and a logic which should take you right up to that last letter.) But there were also letters that were just too sad or disturbing to include——on a Richter scale of 10 for sadness, they scored 11. As it is, there are not a few letters which will distress people, and they are here because to leave them out would be to deny the kaleidoscope of reactions to the phenomenon we call Xaviera.

In any case, however you may view these letters, with unflagging interest or contagious amusement or occasional distaste or, best of all, a nicely rotating windmill of reactions, the important thing is that the letters are real. There has been major editing where part of one letter proved too repetitious of other letters or where the writer rambled off into left field somewhere. And there has been minor editing throughout the book, but mostly to clear up confusing sections or to correct typographical errors. But we have not changed misspellings or grammatical errors, because we wanted to remain as close as possible to the actual spirit and content of each letter.

Of course all names and addresses have been completely changed, to protect the privacy of the writers. Exception: a few instances where the letter was an invitation to speak, and therefore an invitation to a public event.

There was one letter, from a Charlotte, N.C. composer, we wanted to include in the book since he not only had written a song extolling Xaviera, but gave it to her. We figured that since he'd made her a present of the song, we could include it in the book, but our resident corporation counsel——who doubtless got his law degree from Simon Legree Community College——said that would be a **nolo contendere** no-no if the song were copyrighted. We tried to track the composer down to get permission to include his song, but absolutely no luck there. Too bad. It would have been fun to include his musical hosannah to the Happy Hooker, and could have been the first step toward a Broadway musical version of the book, then a movie based on the musical, then a book based on the making of the movie, then a play based on the book, and so on. However, since copyright laws prevent our reprinting it here in its entirety, perhaps a line or two will do for a tease:

> "See the Happy Hooker glow,
>   She can come, she can go . . .
>   [She's] been all 'round the world. . . ."

In that spirit, then, let all flowers bloom. Let it all hang out. And **de gustibus,** as the Latins used to say [between orgies].

—Bob Abel & Michael Valenti
New York City, April 1973

Dear Xaviera,

I'm no nut, just an ex-alky trying to dry out in the California sun (and smog). I just finished reading your magnus opus and all I can say is WOW! and "Hot damn." If there were more women like you around, Xaviera, there'd be a lot fewer jokers on the sauce, I can tell you that. You're just the kind of woman who sends me to bed at night with the certainty of having to change my pajama bottoms in the morning. You dig?

But to wax serious, kid, you've really got it, all of it, from alpha to omega. I haven't enjoyed reading a hot book like that since Polly Adler's "A House Is Not a Home." But your little number is much better because it's much franker. Hell, we're only on this spinning globe a short while, so why not enjoy the carnal lusts and *admit it?* I hate all these hypocrites who go around reading books in plain wrappers. Who do they think they're kidding?

Honey, could you see your way clear to sending me a picture of yourself in the buff? Unless I get to meet you real soon, I may be driven back to the bottle (Just kiddin', baby).

Keep 'em rising, sweetheart,

Charley Billings

La Jolla, Calif.

Dear Xaviera!

Xaviera, have you seen the film, "Deep Throat"? It's playing all over America despite its stupid "X" rating.

I don't say the film is any great shakes as art, but my

husband and I had one helluva time seeing it. We diddled each other to beat the band, if you must know, and I've seldom enjoyed a movie more. Even had some good laughs, as the film does have some good yocks to it.

Now what I want to talk to you about is—how does a gal learn to be like Linda Lovelace and take it all the way and swallow all his love juice without choking or, if the truth be known, even really tasting it?

Right now I can accommodate him only half the way, and while I don't mind the taste of his sperm, it does kind of gag me sometimes. Do you have any idea how I could learn to take the whole root in my mouth? I'd rather he shoot down my throat then I have to handle it the other way. I'm speaking frankly, of course.

If you write me, do it in care of the following post office box number [deleted] because I don't want my husband to know I'm writing you about this. If you must know, he's such a staunch individualist that he thinks people should figure out these kinds of things for themselves. Or, "work them out," as he likes to say.

Very truly yours,

Linda M. Rolfe
Spokane, Wash.

Dear Ms. Hollander,

I just finished reading your book, "Xaviera," and I must say that I truly loved it. I read "The Happy Hooker" also and I really enjoyed that too.

From reading your two books I have gotten the impression that you are a very sincere, honest and witty person.

I really liked your style of writing because you are so honest about telling everything that has happened to you. I think one can get more enjoyment from a book when the author is as straightforward as you were. Of course it helps to lead an interesting and exciting life, as you have. I couldn't believe that one woman could have done all that in such a short span of time.

One thing that I still don't understand is how you and that man made it on the airplane. From the way you described it, it seems impossible. But I guess where there is a will there is a way.

I go to a hospital school of nursing in Champaign and live in a dormitory. Most of the girls on my floor have read "The Happy Hooker" and are now reading your second book, and all of them have really enjoyed both.

I am really looking forward to your next book, "Letters To The Happy Hooker." I'm sure it will be just as good as your other two.

One last thing, I think your a right-on person.

Yours Truly,

Betty Jane Perkins
Champaign, Ill.

VIVA XAVIERA!
(I just finished reading your good new book.)

Jeremy A. Benthem
Los Angeles, Calif.

Dear Xaviera,

Seems to me a lot of dudes have been into your pants, and most of them didn't exactly service you the way you'd like to be serviced. At least you only write about the few guys who made your bells ring.

Well, how'd you like to make a little sporting proposition? I'll buy us a fine old evening on the town, but *you* pay *me* if I don't have the thickest dong you ever laid lips upon. Not only will you have a fine old time chomping on

9

this fat dick of mine, but when I put it in you, you're going to see stars.

I know this sounds kind of fat-headed of me, but you'll find that seeing and sucking and fucking is believing! I've got the biggest cock in the county!

Please write me in care of my business address. My wife has read both your books and she's sure to figure out what her horny-handed hubby is up to.

Yours for mutual explorations,

Hank Crandall

Battle Creek, Mich.

Dear Miss Hollander,

I am a woman of nearly 40 and the truth is I've never had much of a sex life. Although I was married, sex never seemed to be that important.

When your book came out I was staying with some good friends who are about ten years younger than I am, and who tried to get me to read it. At first I made excuses, but then one night I began to read it in bed to make me sleepy, but instead I stayed up the whole night reading it—and masturbating. I must be honest and admit I was masturbating partially because I could hear my friends making love, and between their groans and your stories I was going wild.

In the morning I must have looked terrible. It wasn't only lack of sleep—my head was full of all the wonderful things you've tried, and as I looked at my sexually exhausted friends, I felt lonely and unloved and blue.

You can imagine my shock at the next thing that happened. The wife asked me if I had read the book. I said I had. Hesitantly, she asked me if I'd like to join them that night, as they both had always dug me and wanted to make love to me.

I must have turned beet-red, but I managed to say yes, maybe.

The day was an agony of waiting; I tried to nap, but sex was on my mind.

I'll never forget that night. First I made love to the husband while the wife watched and masturbated herself. The fact that the wife was watching made me so excited that I came almost immediately. Then I made love to the wife, who, if anything, excited me even more than her husband. I thought she was going to nibble me forever, and I had a series of orgasms that were indescribable. Then I watched the two of them make love.

Well, a lot of things have happened since then. The wife has found herself a lover, and three nights a week she goes out to ball him, sometimes not getting home until 4 in the morning. The husband and I go to bed like any married couple—even when the wife is there—and what excites me most is knowing she can hear us fucking and sucking and groaning and panting. I don't mind admitting it also helps my ego to know I'm sleeping with a very handsome man, ten years my junior, while his very pretty wife is sleeping alone in the next room.

So you see, Xaviera, you've helped to change my life completely. I feel wonderfully alive, and the other day when I had lunch with an aunt she told me I look ten years younger, how do I do it. I had all to do not to blurt out: "Fucking, auntie, fucking." She should only know the "magic" formula that is rejuvenating me!

Thank you for liberating me,

Stella Lanigan

Chattanooga, Tenn.

Dear Sir:

I request to know the address of Xaviera Hollander—the author of one of your books, "The Happy Hooker." I request to write to her because I am impressed with her "common sense" and sharp mind. If it is not possible—then please tell me how to reach her.

Tusen Takker.

Arne W. Andersen

Trondheim, Norway

Dear Miss Hollander,

As I suppose everyone else has already said—your book was very interesting, and I think someone would have to be frozen in ice to keep from getting turned on. Even then the coldest iceberg would probably have a little puddle at his feet.

After reading your book at least I'm not suffering from an "I must be sick" complex. I was introduced to bisexual love-making and while I did enjoy it (and later enjoyed doing it), I thought surely there must be something wrong with me. It is still fairly new to me but now I'm not getting uptight about my emotions, but rather trying to enjoy every minute of it.

My husband and I started swinging a couple years ago, but I just wanted you to know that it wasn't out of boredom. My hubby is overly passionate and I brought the idea up; swinging, that is. It seems to me that he can go on forever and I really liked the idea of seeing him, after two women, too pooped to pop. Before, I'd usually poop out and he was still raring to go.

I sure wish there was a woman like you around here—although a lot of my ideas have changed and we've done so much more, sexually, than I'd ever have believed we could—I know I've still got a lot more to learn. Well, anyway, someone like you could really give first-rate lessons.

I sure enjoyed both your books and am looking forward to your next.

Sincerely,

Judy Anne Dincin
Nashville, Tenn.

Dear Xaviera Hollander,

My name is Al Prentice, and I am attending the local Community College. [I am majoring in law enforcement].

In my class called "Moral Problems," we are required to write a term paper on a major moral problem of today's society. Over the Christmas holidays, I read "The Happy Hooker" and to me the book told things that go on in everyday life all the time, but when you put a price tag on it, then society desides that it is illegal and immoral. Then when you look back on history, it has been going on since the start of time on earth.

While I was in the army in France and Turkey, I know that it was legal there and I never heard of any raping going on there compared to the U. S.

I would appreciate it very much if you answered, and look forward to hearing from you.

Yours truly,

Alfred Prentice
Muskogee, Okla.

Lovely Xaviera—

I've tried contacting you before, but I'm sure I just appeared as a nuisance, another john or a voyeur and/or covertly moralistic clinician, or boring combination of these.

13

Since you need none of these, you never called to give me your number. So—

Well, after belatedly reading your book, I find its depth, its honesty and its wit, although coupled with tinges of lonely-sadness or seeking—just as electrifying as your eyes, lips, neck, breast contour, nipples and midriff! With the intellectual and the erotic competing so Kaleido-scopically, I found the magnetism forced me to write in this way. This is my last, but very sincere and *firm,* attempt to make your acquaintance. So—

I am 53, Jewish, still quite virile but would trade all the fuck in the world for the privelege to suck, lick & gently bite *your* entire pussy, in and out, for hours on end, to-gether with 69. (Forgive my bluntness & francness). I am a sociology professor, author of books and articles, con-sultant to industry, therapist to children, fairly comfort-able.

I had a coronary more than ten years ago but I walk a few miles every day, fuck fine but slow and steady, leaving my lover to belly dance the two of us to glory. I have no angina, pills or restrictions. I have a married daughter of 23.

I'm divorced, run around but am bored and lonely—I've been really looking for someone like you. You im-press me as a *real* person and intellectual but not a pseudo —or snob. Your ex-profession is fine, essential and honest —you were as outstanding in your career as I am in mine—

I have no friek-things; they mostly revolt me as they do you, not on perjorative grounds but rather on compassion-ate grounds, what people miss in life. . . . I love perfumes; thin, sleezy nightgowns, revealing and colorful clothes, dresses as well as feminine pants, go cunt-happy from mink and fox! Also velvet, you know—

I am a poet, poetry therapist, a patron of the arts, theatre & classical music. I am an Aries & very strong-minded. So—I feel I qualify, in open and aggressive asser-tiveness, for your list of needs on page 279 of one of the finest books I've ever read. If it sounds like bragging, how in hell would a man you'd qualify under your "prerequisites" be other than open & aggressive?

I'm really sure we'd like each other—wouldn't it be fun to at least meet? Thus, I'd suggest luncheon or cocktails or dinner—you pick the day & I'll pick the place—so, after that we could decide on any further course, platonic, erotic or otherwise!

By now you probably have all the dresses, jewelry, minks, etc. you'd want. We could go, after meeting, to your place for whatever, or plan a getaway to one of the islands—I'm also a hopeless romantic! You are as unusual as a woman-person as your name, Xaviera, but then "X" stands for mystique, also 2-x chromosomes makes a female!

Since I've tumbled over you, couldn't you spare the time for us to meet? I'd love to interact with that facile, administrative brain of yours! The most creative ex-prostitute of our time, bisexual but apparently more heterosexual! Since you are a confirmed & genuine (not using it as pure rationalization) nymphomaniac—I'd hardly ever expect to be able to fully satisfy you, nor have the right to tie someone like you down, even if in marriage; it would have to be an "Open Marriage," at least for your sake.

I can be reached by writing (all you have to do is enclose your card with your number, as "Interior Designer") to: [deleted], or calling, if you prefer, the following number: [deleted]

Please write or call, you incredible Woman of Women, Venus Aphrodisia!

Anticipatedly,

Jonathan Friedberg
Charlottesville, Va.

15

Xaviera,

Why did you not apply the God-given talents into positive sexual research?

It appears to me from reading your book, that you left each relationship (other than servicing clients) as sick sexually.

Certainly your relatives and friends could have been much prouder of a positive application of your gifts.

Sickened reader

Dear Miss "Happy Hooker" Hollander:

I finished your fantastically exciting autobiography just a week ago. Now I see your face on the television screen and in the papers.

Don't think ill of me for writing to you at this time, when you are having difficulties with the U.S. government. I do not expect a personal reply, but could you please drop the enclosed stamped self-addressed postcard in the mailbox, with your autograph. I shall be very grateful.

I agree that prostitution should be legalized because it does serve a useful purpose, but I myself would hesitate joining this profession. Oh, don't misunderstand me. I love sex, and making love. However, I don't think I would want to accept payment for making my lover happy. After all, he makes *me* happy with his body and mind as well. Maybe I should pay *him?*

Another reason why I don't believe I'd earn my living that way is—though I need cash desperately—the fear of catching a dread disease or running into a pervert and/or sex maniac. But most of all, I am a "One-Man Woman." I cannot make love to a different man, or several men, each day.

Marriage turns out fine for some couples. I was wed 18 months ago, but my husband deserted the U.S. Air Force, and then me after barely three weeks together.

Since the last time I slept with him, a year went by, almost to the day, that I was untouched by a man—it was

16

like finding myself locked up in a nunnery! Until last May. I was introduced to a wonderful young man—he is 27 and a gentile, I am 25 and Jewish. Life is now worth living again. I no longer feel sad, depressed and lonely. I never imagined that I'd ever be capable of the love I have for him. And he loves me more intensely than any other man I have known. To top it all off, he is a great, absolutely marvelous lover. With him I have had experiences I'd not even dared dream about. We have done things together I never tried with anyone else. And he is a "One-Woman Man."

But I cannot really compare him with other lovers because there were only two besides him. One was my so-called "husband" and the other my steady boy friend who deflowered me when I was 21. He was only six months younger. That night "two cherries were popped" since I was his very first girl. With this example, I beg to differ with your statement on p. 18 of "The Happy Hooker." Quote: ". . . you would have to walk around like a Diogenes to find a virgin over sixteen."

I may add here that I was to have taken wedding vows in June 1967 with a boy—I do not use the word "man" because he was not. At 27, he was still a virgin. I even had to instruct him in the art of French kissing! After the date had been set, the church selected, the lovely white wedding gown purchased, the rings engraved, and perhaps most painful of all, the announcement with my photo appeared on the Society Page, he suddenly said "Farewell!" for no apparent reason, except "I don't love you anymore." I somehow survived. . . .

As for girls, sure, I like them. I appreciate beauty—be it male, female (I find you very attractive) or a sunset. I have never made love to a woman. I'd be willing to try if I found a suitable partner. I shun picking up some slick chick at a "gay bar." About two years ago, an alleged lesbian approached me, but I had absolutely no desire for her.

Dear Madam, I have taken up enough of your precious time. I would like to wish you a long, productive and enjoyable life. I wish you the children you spoke of on the final page of your fine book. It makes me glad that you love your work of keeping the menfolk satisfied and content—especially if they are refused by wives or girl friends.

More Power to YOU!!!

Very sincerely,

Frieda Laurents
Pawtucket, R.I.

P.S. My first kiss was planted on my lips at age 18. And he was only 14. . . .

By the way, congratulations on the fact that several years ago you had achieved the singular honor of "Best Secretary in Holland."

Dear Miss Hollander:
We miss those marvelous evenings of "Food to go."

The staff of your favorite
Chinese restaurant

Dear Xaviera:
At your swell lecture Tues. nite March 28th you gave me your hotel room telephone number. Do you remember? I called several times and left my ans. service number.

Also I stopped in at your hotel one day but you were out. To assist your recollection, I was the one wearing the hearing aid and who read your book, and sat in the very comfortable black chair just to your right.

It was a great blow, Monday nite to hear over TV that

18

you must leave the country and a very sad pleasure to again see your very lovely and cheerful self on the TV. Now I see, with all the harrassment, you had no time to reach me.

I feel the U.S. was entirely too hasty in denying its citizens the benefits of your lectures, writings and the great potential you have for corrective sexual therapy for so many ailing marriages.

I am reading your book again. Like you, I do not smoke or drink, but nevertheless *please let's have champagne together before you must leave.* I'm 55 and retired now, so I can come anytime to suit your convenience. Any hour Sunday April 23 would be great, or you name it.

But again—please phone any hour and tell my answering service "Tell Mr. William Murphy that Vera called to say he should come to 19D _____?_____ or come to _____?_____ at _____?_____

Also, let me know where and when you are leaving so that I may see you off and wish you everything you ever wanted and so richly deserve.

Sincerely,

William S. Murphy
Hartford, Conn.

Dear Xaviera,

I have just finished reading "The Happy Hooker" and would like to congratulate you on having written the best book on the pleasure game I have ever read. And I've read them all—from "Moll Flanders" to "The Sensuous Woman." Most of them have a dreary sameness about them. You've come up with a new and refreshing approach, plus a sincerity I have only found in some of Henry Miller's early works. You've made your experiences come alive with a candid, totally uninhibited, devil-take-the-hindmost approach.

I especially liked the way you opened and sincerely say things like "I was sucking this big cock." Although we all know things like that happen, to see it in print stated so simply and directly, had a strangely exciting effect on me. It was like looking out of your window and seeing a gorgeous chick naked across a courtyard—a terrific erotic experience when you least expect it.

Your book I read is in its eighth printing. I wouldn't be surprised if it goes to 80 printings, that's how good I think it is. It's about time somebody wrote a book that got down to the nitty-gritty and told the truth about hookers.

I'd sure like to give you a buzz when I get to New York. In the meanwhile, would love to hear from the hottest bird this side of Tokyo—you.

Very sincerely yours,

Vincent Murdock
Newtonville, Mass.

Dear Xaviera,

Last evening I finished "The Happy Hooker" without once putting the book down or intermittently not having a concrete like hard-on—which I had to stuff up my pants when I sat down at the dinner table with my family.

I would love to play a "numbers" game with you: 69 at 53. My wife is 39 without a good fuck left in her, I'm afraid. Hope to see you in bed—7¼ inches, with girth to match.

If you would be kind enough to send your phone number to my address at the University, I will call you

when I'm in New York, for conferences. Although I am

53, I am in fucking good shape. Perhaps a trifle over the hill, but still able to fuck for old glory.

Starved for some horny sex,

Peter P. Hastings, Ph. D.

Michigan State University

Lansing, Mich.

Dear Miss Hollander,

I first heard Alex Bennett interviewing you on WPLJ and got so excited I wanted to call up and talk to you. But I lost my nerve.

Since then I've read your book and just *had* to write to you.

I'm 20 years old, married and have a baby. As I read your book I envied your style of life and still do. I love men but I've always had this urge to do a thing with a really nice woman, a really smart woman. Now I know that if we ever had the opportunity I'd do it with you. I would like my first experience to be a really super one, and I believe that with you it would be really heavenly. You seem to know more about the female body than any man I've ever met.

I know the whole thing is silly because I know we'll probably, never meet. But I had to write and tell you how much your book turned me on, and if I ever do meet up with you I'd love to do a thing.

I know this is equally ridiculous, but I'd love to just talk with you. If you ever have nothing to do and would like to talk with one of your most ardent admirers, just dial area code [deleted]. You can even call collect—but please don't say who you are if someone else answers.

Thank you so much,

Mrs. Virginia (Ginny) Olmstead
Morristown, N.J.

Dear Miss Hollander,

Your book was a real delight to me, but what especially caught my eye was when you referred to "loving to groove on voices" and the fact that you feel you can tell what a person looks like by the sound of their voices.

It reminded me of a story. A few years ago I was dating a girl who had an answering service. I called her so often that pretty soon I got on familiar terms with one of the girls there, a girl named Bessie. I used to love to get her when I called just so I could listen to that voice. I always made my messages as complicated as possible with Bessie, so she would have to ask me questions and just to simply draw out the conversation. One day, after a particularly friendly chat, when I hung up I realized I had a fierce erection.

Sensing that she was aware of what I was doing, I finally asked Bessie for a date. She laughed and at first I misunderstood. "Are you married?" I asked her. "No," she said. Well, to make a long story short, she finally agreed to meet me. But I couldn't understand why she was so amused by the whole thing.

I soon found out. We decided to meet in the anteroom of a midtown restaurant and when I got there there were three or four ladies waiting for their escorts. Since I didn't have the courage to approach any of them (one was an absolute knockout), I had to wait until, one by one, their men friends appeared. Finally there were only two of us left—me and a sedate looking woman of about 55 who looked like a schoolmarm and who sat there calmly and unruffled. After a few minutes, when no one else arrived, I asked her "Are you Bessie?" She nodded.

Very disappointed, I asked the head waiter to get us a table and we went in to dinner. I felt like I was dating my great aunt.

But not for long. Once Bessie began to expand on her life, her job and her basic attitudes toward life, she got better and better looking. It was that terrific voice. It gave her a sparkle not many younger women have. By the time we were half way through the wine, that old familiar feeling in the groin began to return. And I couldn't keep my eyes off that mouth, slightly large, out of which came the voice that had started the whole thing.

By the time we had finished our espresso, I just wanted to get her into a cab, go back to her place and ball her. The wine bolstering my courage, I told her so. We had a delightful exchange about this, until I finally said: "Bessie, if you don't take me home with you, I'm going down on you right here under the tablecloth."

Never at a loss for words, Bessie said: "Well, we can't have that, can we?"

So we cabbed uptown and, after some initial shyness, Bessie turned out to be one of the greatest lays of my life. What I especially enjoyed was the ardent way she sucked me, which seemed especially appropriate considering the circumstances that had brought us together.

All I can say is that Ben Franklin was right about women over 40.

Sincerely,

Don Applegate

Glen Cove, L.I.

23

Dear Miss Hollander,

After reading both of your books, I was wondering if you should ever marry would you expect your husband to be a virgin?

I hope you get a kick out of the idea, as I did when I thought of it.

Sincerely,

Mrs. Francene Howells
Zanesville, Ohio

Dear Miss Hollander,

First I must say how very much I admire you for your frankness and way of living. It is indeed refreshing to find out that the whole world is not filled with prudish women. I surely like your approach to sex and the way you make it clear that nothing is taboo or forbidden any more. Thanks for writing "The Happy Hooker" and fresh thought. It really turned me on more than anything I have ever read before.

I have a sexual problem and I wonder if you can help me reach a decision on what to do about it.

I am a 15 year old white girl who finds Negro men to be fascinating and Oh so attractive to me. They charm me. I want to sleep with Negro men but I am afraid what my friends will say and think about me if I do ball black men.

I have met black men in a nearby Disco-Tek, danced with them, talked with them, kissed them, but that is as far as I have gone with them so far. All of these black young men have asked me to go to bed with them. I admit that I found it hard to say no so far. I wanted to do it with them just as much as they wanted me.

My question is this: Should I go ahead and sleep with Negro men the way I want to so badly, despite what my friends think or say? Or should I continue to say no to

Negro men wanting to sleep with me and I with them just to please my friends?

One other fact you might consider is this. My father is a homosexual with a great yen for young black men. He has urged me to date blacks and bring them home. I suppose that he thinks if and when I do come home with a black man, then he shall also have a chance to make a little arrangement with them. He would make it clear that if they wanted to sleep with his daughter, than they would have to allow him to perform homosexual acts on them first. I would be the prize, after they offer their consent and let him do as he likes.

Please tell me what to do in this matter. I am always so aroused at the touch of a black man and I want to get laid and sexually satisfied as soon as I can. I am burning with desire for black men. I keep dreaming of their beautiful long purple black cocks. Should I also let my father have his way with any black lovers I bring home? Or will I lose them this way?

Many Thanks Darling.

Bye Now Luv,

Edythe Simmons
Dortmund, West Germany

Dear Miss Hollander,
You have opened my eyes about the lifestyle of prostitutes. I am a 21-year-old junior in college, but have never seen a prostitute, and have always thought of them as dirty, evil and disease-ridden people, mostly on dope. I guess I got this idea from the stories I heard about a 14-year-old girl runaway from Cleveland who used to be known in my part of Wilmington as "Boxcar Bertha." (She actually lived in an abandoned boxcar for a while, but Bertha wasn't her real name.)

25

Fortunately, in your book you point out the difference between a call girl and a common whore, but I still have the impression that only the rich and upper classes hear about and can afford call girls. What's a guy supposed to do meanwhile? I hope to be in the rich or upper classes someday, but until I am what do I do about, well, you know.

If you happen to know of any girl who is working her way through the University of Syracuse by selling her body, please let me know. I suspect about a half dozen girls who act too "free" with boys, but I also don't wish to be sued for defamation of character if I'm wrong.

Anxiously awaiting your answer,

Herbert T. Roberts

Syracuse University

Syracuse, New York

Dear Ms. Hollander:

Look what fame does, its become bloody well impossible to get hold of you. Hopefully, miraculously, there will be a major break-through and this letter will somehow reach you. You see, it was a fine and high experience while reading your book to flash at least a little bit on the way you'd created your life, and I'd like to try and do a play along those lines into life. Just from the little I know from your book, and my own life experience in odd delicious places like the Lisbon waterfront or Amsterdam, on those mornings where the sun is hot and full of kisses as you come out the door for the first time, I've had intimations of scenes which could fit either a conventional or environmental structure. But I don't know which yet.

As concerns my credentials, I've done lots of writing, mainly plays, some experimental films, and I try, content and structure wise—as I think you do—to somehow be there in life, not just playing a game of it, and then to reveal it, where one has been. But what can I say here? I mean, if you want I can send you my resume, but I'd rather see you instead. Sad to say though, maybe you don't want a play done.

But if you did, or if we could at least talk about it, and a lot of other questions and thoughts I have, too, well, that would be good for me and I hope for you too. Thus, if you are in Europe and intend to be there for another month or so, do you think you might forward to me an address and phone number where I can reach you when I go over?

Oh, and I should also say that I want to pursue this preferably with you, but if you don't have time, or for whatever reason, could you be so kind as to put me on to someone here in the city whose methods and integrity satisfy you? I would appreciate this very much.

But I hope we get a chance to meet and talk, I truly do.

Sincerely yours,

John Carter Bolton
Norwalk, Conn.

Dear Xaviera,

One night recently, my wife was curled up with "The Happy Hooker" and having a ball. From behind my paper, every once in a while I peeked over at her and knew she was going to be insatiable that night. I could feel a complementary stirring in my groin. Suddenly she looked at me with such pure hatred, got up, flung the book at me and stormed out of the room.

I was thunderstruck. It took me nearly an hour to get her to talk to me through the locked bedroom door, and even then all she would hiss out was "page 77." With my heart pounding, I reread page 77. And there it was: "After all, I had made it with half of Rockefeller Center. . . ." you say.

Xaviera, *I* work in Rockefeller Center. I have worked

27

there for almost twenty years come September. And my wife, while she is normally sweet and understanding, can be a jealous and hysterical woman when she suspects me of wrongdoing.

I know it's a lot to ask, but would you write to her and assure her that we never made it together? I work on the [deleted] floor for the accounting firm of [deleted].

My God, Xaviera, why couldn't you have made it the Empire State or the Graybar building? The fate of my marriage may very well rest in your hands right now.

With fervent hope that you will see fit to help,

A. Russell Harding

Oradell, N.J.

Dear Xaviera,

I want to write to you for several reasons. First of all, congratulations on the success of the two books you have written. I have read and enjoyed both of them. At the end of your last book you said you would be glad to receive letters and that you will be printing another book later this year called "Letters to the Happy Hooker."

You've certainly led a most stimulating life. I'm sure your revealing books have a very definite influence on the lives of their readers. It surely influenced my lovers' lives. My lovers and I get turned on by reading your books, and many times I've had to stop between chapters to take care of their need for sex. I take care of both kinds of sex problems.

Could you please answer this letter. You turn me on so.

Lots of love

Lesley Jean Reese

Hamtramck, Mich.

Dear Miss Hollander,

In "The Happy Hooker" you mention masturbating a dog for kicks. Well, when I was a young boy of about nine I was walking along a rivers edge in North Carolina when I spotted a young woman who was completely naked and bent over on her hands and knees. This alone was enough to shock me, but the thing that left an ever-lasting impression on me is the fact that she was being fucked by a large dog At first I thought they were just playing, faking it. But as I think back to that day I know they were definitely having sexual intercourse. I still remember how red and stiff the dog's tool was as he drove it in and out of her frantically. I didn't make my presence known but hid behind some bushes and watched for what seemed like an eternity. until she cried out and had an orgasm.

Later that night and through all of my adolesent years I would masterbate while visualizing that scene, especially when she made him take it out and he howled because he hadn't come yet. So she let him put it in her again until he fired his load. It was still dripping when he took it out and they both looked exhausted.

To this day nothing turns me on more than viewing stag movies or photos of women participating in bestiality. I have a whole library of books on the subject and I have even tried to convince my wife to try it with a dog. Although she admits she gets aroused while watching movies on the subject, she absolutely refuses to try it.

As an ex-prostitute, were you ever asked to have intercourse with a dog or other animal and if so, did you do it? I'd appreciate any comments you may have on the subject. And, as I have not seen this act since that one time as a child. I am interested in learning of any places that give live shows.

Lindsey R. Kempner

Covington, Ky.

Dear Xaviera:

I happened to catch you on the Howard Smith radio show. You came across as a very intelligent, considerate and beautiful person. Of course I fell in love with you. I am a 20-year-old college student. I have always been very shy, and so have never had a sexual relationship. You strike me as the ideal person to introduce me into the art of love. Forgive me if I am being presumptuous, but I felt I owed it to myself to ask for your help. I have a very athletic, supple body, and therefore believe I won't be an altogether hopeless pupil. You mentioned on the radio show that you enjoyed yourself with young men between the ages of 18 and 23. I dream that I will be one of these.

Love,

Stan Sobachek

My telephone number is [deleted]. Please contact me as soon as possible on any weekday. I shall be waiting impatiently for your call.

Stan Sobachek
Tenafly, N.J.

Dear Miss Hollander:

I don't know if it's a good idea to write you in care of *Screw,* but what have I got to lose? I'm 33 years old, married and a lawyer. I've read your book and just finished reading Part I of your *Screw* interview.

I would love to meet you for a discipline and humiliation session. I've had some experience in the so-called massage parlors, but they were all rather disappointing. The girls for the most part are in bad shape, theres no equipment and, most important, they're no more dominant than a mouse. I need a woman with a really cruel streak in her.

If you decide to get in touch, you can write me at [deleted]. I have a mailing address there under the name of [deleted]. I just took it for the ad; its a very dreary place and I expect to cancel it at the end of March if I don't hear from you. Good luck.

By the way, I'm dark, over six feet tall, and not fat.

Jared Babcock

Jersey City, N.J.

Dear Miss Hollander—

The Lord God put your name in my mind so this is the reason for the enclosed literature. I'm not some old fashion, nutty old woman. I'm fairly young and the mother of six children (no, I'm not Catholic either). This is my second marriage, but before this other life in knowing "Yeshua," my Lord & Saviour, "my Messiah." I knew a lot of men also, but one day I had *no* peace of mind or spirit. I didn't know at the time that someone was praying for my soul. As soon as I mail this note off, I shall continually hold *you* up to my God. *Be assured* there shall not pass one night when I shall not pray for *you*.

I believe these little booklets I have enclosed will speak to your heart, soul and mind more than anything I could say to you. You need not acknowledge this letter if you don't want to. The only acknowledgment I want is to say someday to Yeshua—"Come into my heart & cleanse me from all my sins."

This age we are living in is coming to a rapid conclusion. *"God does not lie."* Keep your eyes on Israel.

I am astounded to find myself writing to you as you might feel in receiving it. May the Lord God through His

Son, thorns cutting into his sacred flesh and drenched in holy blood, touch your heart.

Love in Him,

Mrs. Prudence Grace Alden

Rutland, Vermont

Dear Xaviera,

I want to talk to you about love, Greek-style.

I've read your book and it is indeed very liberated, but nowhere do I hear you endorse Greek-style.

I happen to love it. It gets my rocks off completely, doesn't involve worry about getting pregnant and allows my lover to play with my tits and my clitoris at the same time he's reaming me into ecstacy.

I realize my lovely little anus hole won't sustain this kind of attention, that eventually I'll have to get my sphincter muscle tightened, but right now I must say it's a complete gas. No contraception. Wild orgasms. No worry about complications. I love it. Any decent-looking guy who wants to jam me up the asshole, I'm with him!

Marcella McAndrews

Moline, Ill.

Dear Miss Xaviera,

I have just recently had the pleasure of reading "The Happy Hooker." I have not yet seen you on television, which would be a great pleasure, and getting together with you in person, which would be the greatest pleasure of all. I'd like to, though, even if I have to pay, no offense.

You see I have been curious about your profession and up to a month ago hadn't found anything that explained how it worked very well. Too, I had some misconceptions about call girls and the other types. Then I saw your paperback book and found myself picking up a copy and looking at the picture of you on the back. I gazed in the book and got an idea of what it would be and so decided to buy it, which I did a week or so later.

I didn't regret buying the book because it was a very worthwhile experience in finding out about a lovely and dazzling and very vivacious woman. I found myself attracted to you as I read the book and at times got rather "turned on" with the descriptions of your experiences. I am not a sex fiend, but I do enjoy the warmth and good feeling a woman can provide a man no matter if he has to pay her for the pleasure or the pleasure is his as in a regular date with his girl friend.

I believe I could like a woman like you. What do you think?

Enough for now. I'd be very pleased if you could find some time to reply to this letter. It would be a good thing for me. Being shy, it would give me a really good boost. Not that you haven't already.

> With love in my heart, I am yours truly and sincerely,
>
> Sanford (Sandy) Kiely
>
> Albany, New York
>
> P.S. I am 24 years-old.

Dear Miss Hollander——

I've bought and read both of your books and I feel like I almost know you personally. I've decided the greatest thrill I could have would be to meet you, but of course, that's impossible.

But this isn't strictly a fan letter. I've got a problem that I think only you could help me with and I honestly believe that you won't laugh at me but will take me seriously. My 'fella' and I have been making it together for over a year and I absolutely adore it, but here's the problem: his prick and his attitude toward it. He has an honest-to-goodness beauty and its "just a little" over average, but he's convinced that its a failure and tiny. I know it's *not* tiny because one day, in a fit of anger, I was unfaithful to him and you are *SO* right about not being happy with a smaller prick after having a big one stuck in you.

But anyway, back to my honey. He always makes me feel good, but he has a tendancy to come rather fast at first, and then we go at it again and he's fine. I've told him I'm happy with him, but he's convinced he's a failure, like I said. My question is: Please, Miss Hollander, could you tell me if there's any way I can convince him his prick is big (without telling him about the other guy; he doesn't know) and is there any way I can get him to go longer so he'll start being happier with our sex life? He's so sure he's not satisfying me and so on, that sometimes he gets really depressed about it.

Thank you so much for taking the time to read this letter and if you would write and give me some advice, I would be really grateful and thrilled to death! Thank you.

Sincerely—

Lynn Frazier

Winnetka, Ill.

Dear Xaviera:

Enjoyed reading your book. You lay it right on the line, which is more than some of the junk I've been reading lately . . . (like the "Sensuous Man" does.)

I figured your birthday was in 1942 in either Aries, Taurus, Libra, Scorpio. Or you have quite a few planets in those *sexy* signs. Would you send me your birthdate? No,

34

I'm not an astrologer—don't find it too accurate. Handwriting and Biorythm are a much better gauge on how a person relates to another person. Also will show accident prone days with the latter. No harm in trying it out.

Another book I have is "Numerology" by Vincent Lopex, the band leader, at Hotel Taft. He is 100% right for me this year. Another is Doc. Anderson's book "The Man Who Sees Tomorrow". Claims Las Vegas will triple in population by 1978. (And it's legal in some counties in Nevada—See "Look Magazine" June 29, 1971)

Have been planning to go West to get away from smog, lousey weather and high taxes here in South Carolina. I must say that you remind me of the Scorpio girl . . . I was to have married, who passed away Oct. 11, 1948 at the age of 29. Which left me hung up for quite some time. So—I'm a bachelor, born Jan. 7, 1917—old enough to be your grand-father.

Five planets in Aries-Taurus keeps me feeling young. The few girls I've met in the business were always treated as "ladies" and they in turn treated me like a gentleman, in fact we usually had a mutual admiration society going for us. I'd trust them a mile, which is more than I can say about preachers, cops and politicians. Maybe some day things will change. I'm for giving those ladies a four day week, plus a pension plan for retirement, especially the ones I've met.

I'm enclosing an envelope if you want to send me your birthdate (year, month and day). You don't have to put your return address on it if you don't want to. Wish you lots of luck with your book. Seems to be doing well, as it was the last one left on the rack.

Sincerely,

Ray Quinlan

Greenville, S.C.

Dear Xaveria,

I am 19 and living with my girl friend who is 23. We are happy, enjoy sex together, and experiment a lot.

I have mentioned that I would like to get into other varieties of experiences with others. but she doesn't like the idea of sharing me with others (male or female) and says she couldn't enjoy sex with others just for the sexual pleasures, even though I would like to try it. If I were on my own, I would probably have had a good start at other experiences. but that may come later, one never knows. In the meantime I would like to involve her as well.

We aren't bisexual, but enjoy going to gay clubs because of the atmosphere, and you don't have to compete with others, as in a straight place. As most of the males and females are bi, there are good opportunities for whatever you feel like.

I would really enjoy getting together with other girls there, but don't since she wouldn't like it (even though she gets approached by good looking girls and guys). Is there some way I could get her interested if she could let herself go, and forget about the do's and don'ts stuck in her mind?

If not, I wonder if I should carry on this fantasy myself, and how would I go about getting it together with these girls or with other groups?

Also she doesn't have any fantasies of any kind, which I find strange. Most people have some wild fantasy that they would like to try. Is there some way of stimulating fantasies? Or is it just up to the individual's sex thoughts?

Sincerely (too many fantasies),

Jasmine Marshall

Portland, Oregon

P.S. Your book was fantastic, couldn't put it down even while eating.

Dear Xaviera,

Just a line to let you know that I read both your first book and the publicity you've been getting on the new one.

For some reason or other I have become very interested in you, like probably a million others.

I am a man of 40 years of age and very athletically inclined. I am 5'10" tall, weigh 184, am no Valentino, but certainly won't scare you. I am of Italian stock and have a pleasant manner about me.

What I am trying to say is that I would like to meet you in Canada sometime for dinner and a pleasant time.

I sure would appreciate it if you would accept this letter as one would from a true friend—so the best to you from a new friend, and if I am your friend, I am a good friend.

Love to you, Xaviera,

From

Henry Vigilante
Massena, N.Y.

P.S. If you want, I will come to visit you, no strings, just friends.

Dear Miss Hollander,

I don't know whether or not you received my first letter, but it only said that I don't condemn prostitution or you for being in the business.

I also said that I enjoyed your book. That was an understatement. I loved it; your story was absolutely mind-blowing! It was true and uncensored and that's what I like about books, providing the subject matter is interesting, which your most certainly was!

I got a postcard from the publishing company signed by you. Is that your signature? The card also said that there is a "terrific" interview of you in a men's magazine. However, I'm not old enough to buy the magazine but if I can, I'll borrow someone else's copy and read it.

I wanted to tell you that from the book cover on *Hooker,* you are very pretty and as you wrote in your book, you don't look like a hooker. Happy, yes, but hooker, no.

I don't know if you will personally read this letter, as most celebrities have public relations people who handle mail, but I hope you get it. (It just occurred to me that you already are in public relations yourself!)

I have a very strange image. I can see you in my mind, sitting back to read my letter in your "house". The thought of that gives me a thrill, as I have never written to a *real* hooker before, but living in Las Vegas, I see plenty of them.

I am interested in what you do now. Are you still in the "business"? Are you still a "happy hooker"? Also, is your name really Hollander?

By the way, I talked about your book so much to everyone I know, that now they all call me the "Happy Hooker".

I hope I'm not taking up your time, as I know you must be *very* busy. But if you ever wrote back personally, I think I would flip out!

Thank-you. Good luck in your business.

Sincerely yours,

Mary Lou Baines
Las Vegas, Nevada

Dear Miss Hollander,

First let me introduce myself. My name is Bridget O'Shea and I think we both have arrived at a similar philosophy of life. I first heard you on a talk show where you were discussing your sensational book. No one in America read it more carefully than I did, because I run a similar operation on the Coast. Mine is a lot smaller than yours, naturally, since I don't have the New York freaks to draw on.

The reason I'm so good at it is the same reason you're so good at it—I love it. With me it's more than a profession—it's a way of life. Like yourself, my biggest problem is in finding the right kind of girls, with the elegance and poise to intrigue the type of client we are both looking for —rich *and* horny.

I would be very flattered if you took the time to write me, or to call, and please reverse the charges. My area code is [deleted] and the number is [deleted]. I realize of course that you must have as busy a schedule as I have.

I am really sincere in wanting to build the classiest house on the Coast, and I believe the best way you can learn is from the best. You're the best as far as I'm concerned.

If you are going to be in the L.A. area, I would love to meet you in person. I think we would have a lot of things in common to discuss and I would appreciate any pointers you could give me on running a first-class house.

Love you babe,

Bridget O'Shea
Brentwood, Calif.

AN ADVENTURE: VIRGIN SPRING

From the time "The Happy Hooker" was published I did my best to cope with the mail which arrived almost every day. By now I must have written thousands of letters to readers who were kind (a few were **not** so kind!) enough to write me, congratulating me on my book, telling me their problems, generously offering to go to bed with me, whatever. It has been quite an educational experience getting all this mail, and of course some letters have pleased me more than others. So allow me to introduce one of my favorite letters.

Dear Xaviera:

Whenever I come across something that pleases me, I have to respond in some way. I have just read your book, and I enjoyed it so much that I just had to write and tell you so.

In my whole life I never felt so erotically charged as when I was reliving your experiences with you! The part I really loved believe it or not, was when you were teaching your friend Helga how to make love. That must have been a beautiful experience for you.

I also immensely enjoyed your seduction of young guys. In fact that's what spurred me on to write to you, because I imagined that you were seducing *me*. It felt so great. I sure was jealous of those guys though!

Let me tell you a little about myself.

I'm 19 years old, with better than average looks. I'm quite tall too, about 6' 3" or so. I've got shiny brown hair, along with brown eyes. All this should indicate that I must have millions of beautiful girls swarming all over me. I also can say without being egotistical, that I have a very nice personality. I'm generous, kind and considerate and have a good sense of humor. I love sports too. But I don't have any girls! There is one thing I want more than anything else in the world—to have a girl to love. Why don't I have a girlfriend? The answer is fairly simple—I'm terribly shy with girls. That's it, in a nutshell.

I like girls very much, and I always will. But I don't know when or if I will ever have the confidence to ask a girl so much as to go out on a date with me, never mind ball me or marry me! Sometimes I get so frustrated when I think that after 19 years I have never even so much as kissed a girl! I'm not lying.

I have beautiful dreams at nite about making love to a beautiful girl, sometimes I even hug my pillow intensely and pretend that I'm kissing her breasts. But to think of such a beautiful thing happenning to me in real life—I sometimes find it hard to believe it ever will.

I know its hard to imagine a college sophomore whose never had a girlfriend, well I can't say never exactly. In 8th grade there was a girl who my friends said had a real crush on me. She did, and we got to be good friends for about 2 weeks or so. But it was she who came up and asked *me* to dance that first time. She has since moved away, and I've never even come close to having a girlfriend since then.

I guess school didn't help any. My father sent me to an all-male private H.S. and I'm now attending an all male college. So my chances to even *meet* girls have always been hindered severely. I go to dances whenever the college holds them. Each time, I promise myself that I will meet a girl and make friends with her, maybe even take her back to my room and make love to her. But I break my promise every time and end up walking back to my room empty-handed and empty-hearted.

I've ruled out the possibility that I may be a homosexual, although everyone knows that every human being is bi-sexual to some extent, so I'm not worried about that.

As long as I'm on the subject, let me tell you about

something that happenned to me during my freshman year.

I remember this day very well. It was Sept. 24, 1970, about 2 weeks after school had started. Our school has a swimming pool underneath the gymnasium where the students are allowed to swim every night. One night I decided to go down. The policy, or rule, at the pool is that you are supposed to swim in the nude, for sanitary reasons. Since the school is all male, such an arrangement was possible.

I had never gone "skinnydipping" before and found the idea of it very intriguing, to say the least. I got undressed and jumped right in. Wow, I felt so great! It was such a pleasurable experience for me to be cavorting and splashing in a pool, totally nude, and totally free, that I sprouted a tremendous hard-on! Now there were no girls around, and I was not even thinking about them, but here I am ready to ejaculate the contents of my scrotum at the slightest touch. I couldn't believe I felt so turned on. I was watching my fellow students jumping off the board, their sex organs swinging freely about, limp as can be.

The pool was deep enough so that no one could see my throbbing cock, which of course was a relief, but I started wondering if it was ever going to go down! I thought of jerking off, but I couldn't start playing with myself, attracting the attention of the other guys in the pool. What to do? I couldn't stay in the pool all night!

Well, finally I got used to the sensation of swimming nude and I lost my rod—relief! I hopped out of the pool and into the hot shower, where there were no individual stalls I was scrubbing down my body when this guy next to me started talking about how nice it was to swim in the pool bare-ass. He added that it would be so great if we could get girls too. "Imagine how cool it would be if there were girls here swimming with us."

I did—a mistake. My cock started growing again— slowly. I tried to stop it by thinking about something else, but it didn't work, and soon I was hard as a rock. I was so embarrased. I noticed too that this guy was staring at my monstrous organ, like a guy stares at a *Penthouse* pet.

Then I looked over and saw his cock was as hard as mine. I got a little scared so I left the shower and dressed. After I did the guy, George, came over to me and asked if I would go to the college cafeteria for a friendly Coke with him. He seemed like a good guy, probably knew I was a freshman, so I figured innocently that he just wanted to tell me about school. Well, that's what he did. Then he started asking me if I had a girl friend, and I said no. He seemed surprised, and so did I when he said, "Gee, you shouldn't have any trouble getting girls with a cock like that." He sort of mumbled the last part of that sentence, but I heard it. I just shrugged like it didn't matter. But it was then that I began to suspect a certain strangeness about him. He was a good looking guy himself, by the way.

We left the cafeteria and walked back toward the Gym. I was walking back to my room. George was going to his car. When there was no one around he said to me, "I'm going to ask you something O.K.?"

"Alright."

"Promise you won't get mad?"

"Yeah sure, what?" By this time I knew a bomb was about to drop.

"Well, the thing that turns me on about you . . . is your cock." I pretended to be calm, but actually I was scared stiff. I could foretell his next line.

"Could I . . ."

I didn't let him finish the sentence. "No, I don't do that sort of thing," I said, in a slightly quivering voice. I then started walking faster, away from him. He didn't try to go after me. He just said, "Hey, wait." I didn't want to but I did.

He wasn't mad at all, in fact he understood my fear. He just wanted me not to tell anybody, since he had told me his full name. I didn't rat on him. He explained to me that "he liked to make it with guys as well as with girls"—a line I didn't buy till I read your book. Now I realize that its not that outrageous a thing, if you can keep your head.

What I really wanted, and still do, is my first lay. Sometimes I can almost taste it. Here is what I would like it to be like.

I would enter that room—there she is, waiting for me, waiting to be devoured like a thick, juicy steak. Her eyes glistening brilliantly, sensuously, at the sight of my huge cock, which is now throbbing in mid air. She shakes her head violently back and forth, her long silky hair erotically hiding her face, which is exquisitely beautiful. I gently lay down beside her, part her georgeous hair to reveal a delicious, sensuous mouth, drooping open, watering. Her full lips surround an erotic tongue, waiting, dying to be sucked on. My mouth is drawn to hers like a powerful magnet and I keep it there, giving her millions of erotic kisses. I then start kissing her entire body—her neck, her ears, arms, belly ass, breasts, and all this is leading her up to an explosive orgasm, which occurs when I plunge into her beautiful pussy, licking her clitoris with my super erotic tongue movements. She comes so violently that she starts screaming with joy which makes me come, too, and we haven't even started yet!

I deeply inhale the scent of her wonderfully perfumed hair. I start putting it in my mouth, tickling her firmly erect nipples with it, and wrapping it around my cock! She then goes down on me. Her tongue teases my rod, swirling around it several times, and then starts sucking hard. I soon come in her mouth, and she is so busy coming, too, that she doesn't mind swallowing my sperm. Just wonderful! Then tired as we may be, I intently climb on top of her gorgeous bod, and start pumping slowly at first, then more rapidly unceasingly, savagely This causes her entire body to explode like a hydrogen bomb, and she passes into a deep fulfilled slumber as I whisper words of love into her ear and then fall asleep myself, my lips touching her breasts.

In the morning we would do it again—start off the day with a good, healthy bang. We would eat each other's bodies like hungry wolves, come, and then arise from bed, ready to go out and grab the world by the ass! We'd be totally renewed and invigorated, almost as if reborn!

That's my idea of the human sex act. Pretty good for a guy that's never done it, wouldn't you say? I probably sound like Cassanova—aggressive and powerful. Irresistible. But the fact is that I'm basically very introverted and quiet. I can be aggressive sometimes, like when I'm playing basketball, but other than that I'm just a docile, subdued individual, who would rather listen than talk, rather be touched than touch, rather be led than lead. I think that this is my problem with girls. I just can't be aggressive enough to even talk to a strange girl. I would rather hang around and hope some cute girl will spot me and come over and talk to me. I suppose this happens, but not nearly enough to expect it to.

I can assure you that my sex drive is very high, because I often get hard just staring at a bikini-clad woman at the beach. I relieve my intense sexual feelings by masturbation, as most guys do. But that really doesn't satisfy me. I want to give myself to a woman! But I eat my heart out because I can't find one. Maybe subconsciously I hate girls, or maybe I'm waiting for "Miss Perfect" to fall on top of me. I'm not sure at all. One thing I'm sure of, though, is that I want to make love to a woman soon, because I've never felt the desire so intense as right now. I seem to have an irresolvable conflict, but I can't believe it's that bad.

How come I've never raped a girl? Well, like I've said, I could never be aggressive enough to do it. Besides, I would never think of hurting an innocent girl just to satisfy myself.

Now the big question is—why am I spilling my guts like this to you, a complete stranger? Well the pressure just built up so high that I just had to let some steam out. I had to get this off my chest to someone. I wouldn't want to tell my parents because they just wouldn't understand, even though they're good parents. I had to tell someone like you, who has been through everything imaginable and wouldn't be shocked at something like this.

The impression of you I received from the book was that you are a person who is very kind, loves people, and loves sex. You would be the perfect person to relieve me of my virginity. I could just picture you ravishing my body aggressively, and teaching me how to communicate with women, and how to be more aggressive, and how to love so much that I would no longer have any problem with girls. That would be the most divine thing ever to happen to me—being taught the act of love by an older, experienced woman—you.

I suppose, however, that this would be too much of a miracle for me to expect, since I'm not even sure that you are reading this letter.

However I will thank you again for writing such a beautifully erotic book. It turned me on so much. I hope that if I finally do meet a girl, that she will have read it, and be as uninhibited and loving and understanding as you.

Love and peace,

Phillip Roberto

Garden City, N.Y.

Well, by the time I received Phillip's letter, it was March or April—a few months after my first book had been published. I'd received hundreds, perhaps thousands of letters by then, but his really turned me on. Rarely has a letter—this one, written by hand on yellow-lined paper—gotten me so excited.

The week I got this letter I had been "behaving particularly well"—in other words, I'd been having very little sex, with the result that I was more than a little horny or, as the English say, "randy." As I recall, the reason for this was that there was no one around I especially wanted to sleep with.

However, it wasn't just a case of my being slightly "in heat." Phillip's letter really got to me. It came from an innocent 19-year-old boy describing how he wanted to make love to a woman. In fact the more I thought about him, the more excited I got by his letter and I decided to make his fantasy come true. His letter had contained his dormitory phone number, so I would be able to contact him simply by picking up the phone.

Even though I was busy preparing lectures and doing publicity for the book, I decided I would definitely devote some time to this young man and his carnal cause.

I phoned him one Sunday night at his college and discovered that the number he had given me was a booth in his fraternity house. One of his fraternity brothers answered the phone. Since I had no idea whether Phillip had been telling me the truth when he'd described himself as tall, good-looking with dark hair, I decided to ask the young man on the phone if Phillip was good-looking. I, of course, identified myself as the author of "The Happy Hooker."

He didn't exactly answer my question. Instead he got all excited on the other end of the phone, shouting, "Jesus, my God, he'll love to hear that!' But unfortunately Phillip wasn't around. "He's having dinner with his folks," I was told. "You know, it's Sunday night." He suggested I leave my number so that Phillip could call me right back. Instead I told him to have Phillip call me the following evening, Monday, at 9 o'clock sharp.

Once again I asked him what Phillip looked like. Was he attractive or homely? I said he'd written me he was kind of handsome and I just wanted a second opinion. The boy replied that Phillip **was** good-looking and tall . . . he was also very bashful. He stressed the point that Phillip was very, very shy. And guess what? This was what turned me on most. I guess I felt like a dirty old lady, waiting with anticipation for the next evening.

Sure enough, at 9 o'clock sharp on Monday, the phone rang. I was alone in my bedroom and I answered in a very low, sexy voice. I could hear Phillip's voice shaking over the phone. He stuttered, "Xav-Xaviera, is it re-really you? I mean, you re-really called me up. I can't believe it!"

I assured him it was indeed Xaviera at the other end. Then he blurted out: "What did you think about my letter? Maybe I shouldn't have written so bluntly, with all that stuff about erect penises and all, because now I realize that you are a lady." He hesitated and then continued, "Forgive me, but I was so uptight and I felt like I knew you so well after reading your book. You're the only person in the world who can help me. Can I please come over and see you?"

"Okay, Phillip, come over and see me tomorrow night. First call around 10 and be at my place around 11."

"So late? Can't I come over earlier? Please let me come over earlier."

"Okay, call me at 9 and be here at 10."

"Great," he replied. "Just tell me what I should wear. Do you want me to wear something special?"

"Just be yourself and be clean all over."

He had a very nice voice, I must say, but the poor kid sounded **so** nervous. In my case I was so excited that night that I ended up masturbating after I'd hung up the phone. I couldn't stop thinking and fantasizing about him. What would he really be like? One of the reasons I hadn't told him to come over that same night was that I liked the anticipation!

The next night, around 9 o'clock, I got a call from a girl friend of mine and she didn't get off the phone until about 9:30. A few minutes later, Phillip called. He apologized for being late and stuttered and stammered apologies for the fact that my line had been busy and the booth in the dorm occupied. I asked him, "How do you look tonight?"

"Squishy-squashy clean. I rubbed and scrubbed myself, took three showers, gargled with Scope, brushed my teeth two times, cleaned my toenails and fingernails, because I know you like clean men. And here I am, as clean and fresh as a newborn baby."

I purred, "Are you as innocent as a baby as well?"

"Pl-please, please, that's why I have to see you!"

Now that's what I would call a cry for help, and I wasn't about to refuse. My body was positively tingling with anticipation, and I could hardly wait for the doorbell to ring. All I wanted was to be all alone with my young prince, Phillip.

Truth to tell, though, I was in a pretty nervous state

when the doorbell finally rang. Just why, I couldn't say. I was certainly dressed for the occasion. I was wearing a long, orange negligee, sleeveless showing plenty of décolletage, and I looked pretty slinky. You could see my whole body right through the gown. I couldn't help wondering, is he really attractive, or did his friend just put me on?

When Phillip entered the apartment, I was genuinely dazzled. He was truly a beautiful boy. Quite tall, as he'd said, with a lovely, youthful face, dark questioning eyes, under heavy, black eyebrows. He was broad-shouldered, with slender hips and long legs, extremely well-built. Phillip wore a blue turtleneck sweater and dark blue trousers, with a yellow slicker. He shook my hand and obviously didn't quite know what else to do with himself. His hands were damp and warm. (I noticed he had big hands and feet and a nice, big nose— my favorite attributes for a well-shaped man).

I told him to take off his coat and relax. "Have a seat by the bar while I get you a drink."

"I'm like you," he said. "I don't drink and I don't smoke."

"Okay, how about some Seven-Up, apple juice or some orange juice?"

"Oh, I'll drink anything you want me to," he whispered.

"Come on, Phillip, you have a will of your own— don't let me make all the decisions."

At this point he asked me to please call him Phil, and I readily agreed. And then he settled on having some apple juice and sort of arranged his tall, gangly, body in a quasi-nonchalant pose against the barstool, with his legs spread apart, his hands tucked away deep inside his pockets. I tried to persuade him to take his hands out of his pockets, saying, "You're not a peasant or farmer," but he kept them there safely hidden away.

I served him his juice and when I set the glass down on the bar, he noticed that there were sets of photographs lying under a plate of glass. Some were of me, partially in the nude; others of me and Larry and some girl friends, or me on the beach. Phil seemed fascinated by them, saying, "Oh, my God, you're so beautiful. You're far more beautiful than the picture on the cover of the book. I dreamed about you all last night and wondered how you'd be, what you'd be like."

At this point, I placed myself right in between his long legs, my back to him, and pushed my body against his. Through the smooth, thin material of my gown, I felt his big, erect penis against my buttocks. It was sticking up like an arrow. He certainly didn't have any problems in becoming aroused.

I was very aroused, myself, but I didn't want to touch the large bump in his pants because that would have been too abrupt, too sudden. "Tell me, my little virgin boy," I murmured, "what is it I can do for you?" At that moment, I took his hands out of his pockets and planted them on my hips. He held them there stiffly, still shaking nervously.

"Come on, Phil, relax, will you? Your hands are like two vibrators. If you want a vibrator, I'll teach you how to use one, but not on my hips."

"What do you mean?"

"Stop being so nervous. Relax and finish your juice."

He let go of my hips with one hand and took a long swallow of juice, his teeth chattering against the glass. Boy, was this kid shaky. And, the more nervous he was, the more turned on I became because I knew this was genuine innocence, not faked—the real thing—and I was loving every moment of it.

I told him to put his hands back on my hips. "What do I do now?" he asked, sheepishly. "Now, move your hands around. Explore my body, try to feel what a woman's body actually is like. You may have looked at a woman's body, but now really feel it, touch it, move your hands up and down." I put my hands on top of his and made him feel my hips, my thighs, my ass, my belly, my tits and finally, my erect nipples.

I was still fully dressed. All of a sudden, I turned around, put my arms around his neck and made him kiss my arms, my neck, my shoulders. I said softly,

"Kiss me, touch me, hold me." He did so, clumsily, his big hands almost pushing me instead of caressing me.

"Take it easy . . . don't push me. Let your fingers run through my hair," I said, as I lifted up the back of my hair and offered my neck to his mouth. I then stepped away from him, leaned forward and planted a kiss on his mouth. Both our mouths were closed. His lips were trembling and I decided it was time for the big seduction scene in the bedroom.

I stopped kissing him. "Did you ever really kiss a woman?" I asked. He said he hadn't. "I can't believe it—a young, good-looking boy like you never kissed a woman. But why not?" He told me that he got aroused thinking about kissing girls, but when it came to actually putting his fantasy into practice, he was too scared. He didn't know if it was something psychological, but he'd always been too shy to approach a girl. He was afraid of being rejected.

So I told him, "No girl would reject you for just wanting to kiss her. Maybe she'd balk at going to bed with you, but she certainly wouldn't mind being kissed. Have you ever thought about dating an older girl? A good-looking boy like you, especially one who looks so young and is so well-built, would be appealing to a good many older girls."

I suggested that an experienced girl, maybe in her mid-twenties, would probably go crazy over him. He admitted that I might be right. Every time he went to a dance or after a football game, lots of girls seemed to find him attractive. However, when it came time for him to respond, he sort of felt as if they were maybe making fun of him. Perhaps they just wanted to tease him and see if they could make a fool out of him.

How could he know if he'd never tried it? "Okay, today I'm going to give you your first lesson. And maybe I'll give you a few more lessons someday." But I cautioned him that after he left my house as a man, he had to get out of his shell and start to approach girls on his own. "I hope I won't be the first and last lover in your life!"

I then took him by the hand and led him into my bedroom. I slowly started to undress him. I removed his blue sweater and watched him carefully as he took off his shoes, sitting on the edge of my bed. Suddenly, he looked up at me questioningly. It seemed he wanted to say, "What is going to happen to me now?"

I could see he was impressed by the king-size bed and the mirror and the green light I'd turned on, and last—but not least—by me. I put on some soft background music and closed the door. No one would disturb us—not even my roommate if she were to come home.

I then slowly slipped out of my orange negligee. I did this in a very sexy way, giving him a seductive striptease. I pulled the orange material over my head in such a way that first my legs were revealed, then my pubic area, then my belly and breasts and finally, I was nude, slowly and excitingly. Phillip kept on his undershorts, almost too embarrassed by the huge bulge I could see. He made me smile because he was so cute. I would have loved to fuck him right then and there, but I decided to go easy on him; we had to spin it out as long as possible. Due to his innocence and anxiety, he would probably reach a climax within a few minutes.

Once we got into bed, I suggested gently that he should take off his shorts, which he did. Much to my amazement, he covered up his big cock with one hand. "Don't worry," I said. "After all, you're not Burt Reynolds in the centerfold of **Cosmo.** You're just with me . . . with a woman, not with an audience. Feel me, touch me."

By this time, he was becoming more relaxed and seemed to be losing some of his inhibitions. So I bent forward and took his lovely face in my hands to give him his first real kiss. His head was resting on the pillow and I bent over him, my breasts pushing softly against his chest. With one hand, I tenderly caressed his big, erect prick and with the other I cupped his head as I kissed him.

For a while, we explored and kissed one another, our

bodies barely touching. Then I slowly began my way down, caressing his body with my tongue. I made sucking little movements with my puckered mouth, my right hand gently stroking his nice, strong, hairy chest. He shivered and started giggling, explaining that it tickled. I told him not to mind, that the erogenous zones of the body absorbed sensation according to method of caress. He laughed when I tickled him again. I realized that I had to stroke him much more firmly, without teasing him. Young men seem much more ticklish around their nipples, stomach and balls than older, more experienced lovers. They devote more time to straight fucking than to caressing. As they say, a stiff cock doesn't think.

I massaged his beautiful body, stroking him from his shoulders onto his hardened nipples, kneading his balls and navel gently, until I finally got to his penis—a gorgeous, clean, circumcised cock. It stood up proud and perfect, the head hard and dark, full of passion, ready to explode any second. I put my warm tongue around it, tasting the lovely lubrication of his hot cock. I then guided his right hand toward my vagina.

My young Phil was still lying on his back, passively, content just to let things happen to him. His big prick looked like a pyramid. I lay beside him and at least now his right hand was touching my cunt, while I still had mine on his cock. But then I moved away and started kissing him all over again. After another tour of his body, I now rolled over on my stomach and put myself between his legs, my thighs around one of his upper legs in a firm grip. After a moment of squeezing his thigh with mine, I gently pulled his legs apart and started to play with his balls. Again this seemed to tickle him and he began to laugh. Once more, I had to caress him more firmly. My tongue flicked over his balls and then backwards, past the ridge to his ass. There I held still for a second and proceeded to slide my lips over his huge penis until I reached its base. I could feel his balls literally vibrating and seem to grow in my mouth and hands.

Phil began to moan and he grabbed the pillow next to him, squeezing it in uncontrollable excitement. My baby was so turned on both emotionally and physically that he couldn't contain his passion any longer—actually he'd shown more endurance than I'd expected—and now I was experiencing the jism shooting out of his cock into my mouth. It was beautiful and warm and plentiful. I half-swallowed it and half-dribbled it out onto his belly. It was thick and virile and certainly looked fertile enough to produce many babies. I hadn't seen sperm like that, so thick, in a long time; it almost reminded me of yogurt. It was the first semen from a virgin boy into the mouth of a woman, and I knew this had to be the beginning of a wildly exciting night.

My lover lay there, exhausted but thrilled. He looked at me and asked, in a slightly guilty voice, "How am I going to turn you on? How can I satisfy you, since I've already come?"

"Come on now, you're a young, strong boy. That's only once. I'm sure you can come more than once."

"Okay, let's try it."

Within five minutes of his first climax, young Phil finally devoted some time to my body. Still a bit clumsy and very naive, he put his finger as he'd done before, near my clit. But this time, I taught him how to find the "man in the boat"—the clitoris—without hurting me and without pushing. I made him take a good look at my cunt. I opened the outer lips of my vagina to show him my bright pink cunt and clitoris—very stimulated and therefore enlarged and hardened and not too difficult to find. I guided his finger to it and showed him how to softly but firmly move his finger from left to right over the little knot, now and then putting that same finger in his mouth to taste me.

My ardent lover immediately got a hard-on again. I let him play with me for a while and taught him how to kiss my back, caress my neck and blow kisses in my ear in the same way I'd done this to him previously. So I'd reversed the game!

While he was attending to me, my fingernails softly scratched his back, something he enjoyed tremendously. His body wasn't ticklish anymore because I knew by this time just how to caress him—firmly, but in a very erotic, stimulating manner. I even pressed his nipples between two fingers and sucked and nibbled on them for a while. This made Phillip laugh and he told me it made him feel kind of funny. I asked him to describe the precise sensation he felt when I tickled or gently bit his nipples. He said he felt funny and strange, almost weird, yet pleased and excited. He told me he had never had this feeling before in his life. To me, this was pretty obvious since he was a virgin. After all, who had made any effort so far to turn him on, caress his balls and suck his cock? I was probably the first female, besides his mother, to even see his penis.

Still, he hadn't gotten to fuck yet in the classic sense of the word—he hadn't been in me yet. By this time, after I'd taught him several ways to turn a woman on, his cock was as big or even bigger than it had been when I had made him come the first time. And his playing with my clitoris, although sometimes a little awkwardly—losing hold of it—had turned me on very much and I was even more juicy than before. The first time around, I'd been left "hanging," if you can call it that, because I'd devoted myself to giving him a really thorough blow job, wanting all the pleasure to be his. However, now I wanted to come badly.

While he rubbed my clitoris, giving me cold shivers all over my body, I continued stroking his body and caressing his penis with my other hand. And now the shudders moved subtly into the warm feeling of a mild orgasm. My breasts were hard and the nipples swelled and it was what you might call a "warmer-upper."

But now, after I'd come once, I was even hornier. So I placed his hands almost under the pillows, held them down firmly and whispered, "Okay, let it just happen again." I then climbed on top of his cock and put it all the way inside my hot cunt. I saw him look at the mirror above the bed, a big, gold-colored mirror, and I could

58

see his excitement as he became even more aroused watching me riding him. I bent my body backwards so that my head almost touched his feet and my feet were stretched out under his arms. In that way, he could penetrate at a deeper angle than the usual forty-five degrees.

Then I'd come back up again, face to face, and then backwards again. Sitting on top of him, I'd almost squat on the flats of my feet, like an Indian. Then I'd sit down on his cock, then rise up on it, riding his cock that way in an almost vertical movement. This, by the way, is something that lovers hardly ever think of doing in bed, but take my word for it—it's very exciting. What you do is, you put your feet firmly on the bed and hunch yourself backwards up and down. With strong young Phillip, I put my hands on his broad shoulders, which gave me a better hold—otherwise I'd have lost my balance and fallen backwards.

When I was about ready to climax, I moved my body forwards over him and my head reached his face. I kissed him on the mouth and at the same time I stretched out my legs all the way, right on top of his legs. I closed my legs, and in this way, not only would his penis deeply penetrate my vagina but also the base of his cock would rub against my clitoris because of the vibrating movements I was making.

It was absolutely wonderful. His cock had been so big and strong and nice that I could feel every part of my body shaking and trembling with emotion. When he finally came, again I felt that wonderful sperm, warm and pulsating. It was an absolutely gorgeous climax. The kid was perspiring and was really exhausted. This orgasm was a lot more tiring than his blow job, because I started to make him work as well. I had shown him how to move his body while I lay on top of him. I was in control, but he had to work.

We rested after this and he was full of praise for me. He couldn't believe what was happening to him and when I told him I was leaving soon for Holland, he almost began to cry—like a little kid whose toy is being taken away for having been a bad boy. I said that if I'd met him six months ago, I'd have kept him, and I really meant it. I'd have spoiled him, given him anything he wanted. He reminded me of David, a former young lover of mine. I am very easily attracted to young boys, particularly if they're innocent and virginal. I guess they're my weakness—''There is nothing better than popping a cherry. . . .''

Anyway, I got out of bed and got Phil and me a drink —some more apple juice—and I asked him if he was hungry. He said he was starved. I could very well imagine that he was. With all that sexual activity, he certainly needed something to revive him. I went to the fridge and got him a big piece of apple cake and some Dutch Gouda cheese and we both started devouring the food to give us strength for the next round of sex.

And, indeed, about half an hour later, there he was again . . . erect. This time I wanted to make the kid really work. So I told him to get on top of me and rest on his knees, because he was all set just to flop right on me. I taught him how to crouch on his knees. Then I put a pillow underneath my behind. This is one of my favorite positions, with my legs wrapped around the man's body, actually around his midriff. This way, his penis can penetrate nice and deep. I made Phil move in and out of me and when he began to pump faster and faster, I told him to take it easy, go slow, hold back from coming. I asked him to move his cock in and out its entire length, almost letting it slip out of me. That was very teasing and exciting, I told him.

Finally, he really got the knack. He began to learn just how to titillate me. In fact, eventually I had to tell him to stay all the way inside me and not slip out, because I didn't require any more teasing since I was set to come any moment now. He had a big smile on his face, as if he'd won a great victory. And just then I told him to stop!

Now I showed him how to rest on his knees and I also got on mine, and we came together, belly to belly. I was afraid he'd slip out but since he was so big and since I was in control again, keeping my body very close to his, he did not slide out and we were able to go on fucking for another ten minutes.

Now I was lying on my back again, and he was pushing against me too heavily and I had to tell him to hold me more gently, and not rest all over me and squeeze me to death in the process. Despite my criticism of his love-making techniques, however, Phil was loving every minute of my tutorial!

Later on, I taught him to fuck me doggie style on our knees and while doing it this way, I bent forward and reached backward, getting ahold of his balls. They were like hard-boiled eggs——and rather hot as well. I was squeezing his balls with my fingers and rubbing and caressing the little ridge in between his balls and his arse, and I could feel he was about to come, so I told him to stop screwing me and to think of something sad, like a funeral, and not to come because I didn't want this to be over. "Let's wait a little while."

I told him to lie down next to me and then, after a few moments respite, we resumed our love-making, with him on top of me. However, just as we were about to reach our climax, he leaned more and more forward and almost pushed his big shoulders through my chin. I reminded him again to be gentle. I said I didn't want to turn him off, but I had to teach him how to caress and fuck properly. "Lean on your elbows, but never put your chunky shoulders right on a girl's face. You could choke somebody that way!"

We came for the third time together in a beautiful orgasm and this time he didn't jump off me right away——I taught him how to rest on his elbows after climaxing and hold me in his arms.

That night we fucked four times until we finally fell asleep, or rather **he** fell asleep. I was too stimulated and excited. I got up and began to do some things around the house. By this time, my roommate had come home and I let her peep into the bedroom where the soft green light threw a gentle glow on my beautiful boy, sleeping spread out on the bed, with pillows thrown all around his body. He was tightly hugging one of the pillows. She kept repeating, "How pretty he is, how lovely," so it gave me double pleasure to watch the kid sleeping there and to see the approval in her eyes. It seemed I'd made a good choice in my love pupil.

The next morning, we awoke at 10 o'clock—we had gone to bed at 5 A.M.—because the telephone was ringing. I answered it, then decided to feed Phil some breakfast. But I didn't want him to get dressed, as I had nothing planned for that day until 2 P.M.

After giving him a good breakfast, I said, "Okay, let's take a shower. We'll wash ourselves completely and then we'll go back to bed." I figured we could have one more go at it.

I enjoyed rubbing him down and soaping his cock. I even sucked it a little and watched it grow immediately. I washed him all over and he gave me a good back rub, and then we dried each other off and went back into the bedroom. I wanted to teach him one last thing as a farewell present, because I knew I'd never see the kid again.

So far I had shown him at least seven different positions, which was quite a lot for a beginner, and now it was time for me to teach him "how to give head": how to perform cunnilingus while I ate his cock—that is, how to perform good old 69! He'd asked about eating me after we had made love several times the previous night, but I hadn't let him go down on me after he'd come inside me. I didn't feel particularly clean at that time and I was simply too tired to get up and douche. I don't consider any aspect of sex "dirty," but somehow I prefer 69 as a **pre-play** rather than **after-play**. But now it was morning, and I was fresh and squeaky clean, and eager to teach him, and horny as hell—for a change.

As we lay down on the bed and started to kiss and hug, I slowly placed my body in a position where my pussy lay opposite his face and his cock was practically in my mouth. I spread my legs apart and told him, "Now that you know where my clitoris is—you touched it last night and looked at it and made me come—now I

62

want you to place two fingers all the way, deep inside my cunt, and gently move them in and out. I want you to know what a woman feels like with your hands, as well as with your cock." He opened the lips and softly pushed his long fingers inside my vagina. At first, he hurt me a little bit, but I quickly got excited and juiced up.

While his fingers stimulated my vagina, I showed him how to work my clitoris with his tongue, not neglecting to tell him at the same time to keep moving his fingers inside my cunt, as if his penis were penetrating me. He now knew how to find my clit with his tongue and I was astonished to find that, innocent as he was during the previous night, he had turned out to be an excellent pupil. Very few men learn that quickly—they're usually pretty clumsy for a long time. I must say that young Phillip was a quick learner, but I guess it was because I am a hell of a good teacher! In this way, with me sucking him and Phil eating me, we came again together. His sperm even gushed into my long, blonde hair.

This was to be the last time for the day, because half an hour later my lecture agent called me and wanted to drop by to give me my check for a lecture I had given in Detroit. So I told Phil, "Okay, let's get dressed. I'm sorry, but we've got to come down to earth again."

When the lecture agent arrived, Phil was sitting in the living room, fully dressed and trembling slightly, but this time from fatigue rather than nervousness. We all had coffee and I talked with the agent, who seemed very pleased with the way my lecture had gone. He asked me if I'd give him a farewell present—going to bed with him—and I told him that I was sorry, but I couldn't. I explained, "You see, this young college kid here, well, he's a "Happy Hooker" fan and I am crazy about him and I'm faithful to him." And with that, I stopped the horny agent in his tracks!

A few minutes later, Phillip put on his yellow slicker and walked down the corridor in his coltish stride, after kissing and hugging me farewell. I made him promise to write me wherever I'd be about his experiences, and I told him that, with all the lessons I had given him, he should now be completely confident in himself and not worry about girls rejecting him. I said that a boy like him should hardly ever be refused. If a girl didn't want to fuck him, she certainly wouldn't refuse to kiss him! He was a beautiful kid and now he'd become a man— the most important thing of all. His letter had aroused me, and although I knew instinctively that this was a boy with problems, I felt they were the kind that could be easily solved with careful handling, and with the right amount of love and devotion.

I don't think a beautiful creature like him should have any major problems with girls for the rest of his life. Maybe he shouldn't take things so seriously, especially when refused. He should just go ahead and enjoy himself, and meet as many girls as possible. At least this is what I would hope for him.

Some weeks later, when I was back in Holland, I received my first letter from Phillip since he'd come to class with me. It was a joyous letter, and a joy to receive. He sounded very happy.

Dear Xaviera:

Huff, Puff . . . Ahh . . . and he, Phillip J. Roberto, on April 26, 1972, entered the apartment in awe. He rode the elevator up alone, watching the numbers fly by . . . 11-12-13-14-15. Am I really here? 16-17-18 . . . what will she be like? 18, will I come in my pants when she opens the door? 19, last stop. Everybody off, here's your chance, take a deep breath and try to get that glazed look out of your eye. Knock on the door and let whatever happens happen. WOW.

And the following afternoon he departed, physically, mentally, spontaneously and spiritially fulfilled, on cloud nine in total ecstasy, happy, an indescribably powerful feeling surged through his body as he glided up Third Avenue on that brilliant sunny day. He wasn't just walking, he was walking on water as Peter tried to do and failed. His eyes gleamed, a cute smile crossed his face. He could have seduced any pretty maiden within view, simply by batting an eyelash at her. Napoleon, Alexander the Great, Caeser, Atilla, Muscellini, Bernadette Devlin . . . none of them ever felt the supreme total power that this guy felt, had and exhibited. He had walked in as an infant child (but horney) but came out as an aggressive, beautiful, confident, sexual animal. He pulled a reverse of March, he'd gone in like a lamb and come out as a lion. What a man, what a transformation. The ancient alchemists could not have done a more super job of changing their rocks into gold. Even if they had succeeded they could not have come close to doing what Xaviera did with Phil's rocks. It was like getting chess lessons from Bobby Fisher, a guided tour of the United States by George Washington, or a Congressional Metal of Honor from the President. It was too good to believe, too impossible to believe, too outrageous to believe and too beautiful to believe—but it had happened. Irreversibly . . . undoubtedly . . . fantastically . . . it is something that happens once in a lifetime.

Ahhhh. . . .

Greetings, Xaviera. How is life in the land of the Dutch? I hope you have a few dynamite boyfriends over there to keep you warm at night. I have so much to tell you that I don't know exactly where to start. But I'll just dig a spot and go from there. First of all, let me say that I've always wanted to be envied, but no one ever had any reason to envy me before, that is, until now. You could say that I've become somewhat of a celebrity. A legend, an idol here in the horney, hallowed halls of this school. Right now I could write the HOW TO SEDUCE THE HAPPY HOOKER book and earn a little spending money from all my super-horney friends, such as: 1. Bill Guinness (Ahh, Wow you really made the big time didn't you, Philly?)

2. Guy Richmond, (That's fantastic, man, just fantastic. Your getting Xaviera is like me making it with Jane Fonda (his idol).

3. Fred Guest—Hi, stud, how are you?

4. Milt Rodgers—I don't want to talk to you, you lucky bastard . . . you cocksucker.

5. Bob Lemond—Gee, you'll be known by something besides your marks when you leave here. Why don't you teach that course in written communication? (Which I'm taking now and have a measily C-)

6. Jerry Alessi—who I wish I had there with me because he's such a nice guy, cute too by the way. Let me shake that hand of yours baby. Say I know a lot of johns don't I? (Not as many as you do though).

Xaviera, it's just unbelieveable what those 12 hours did for my popularity. I gained confidence, soul, psyche, you name it, it's been changed for the better. I could go on for pages and pages telling you what a wonderful person you are and what I thought of our experience together, so I will. First off, you don't have to be told that I was scared as hell. I felt like I was just going to melt into a puddle and when you answered the phone, I did. Your voice is so warm and full of energy, so's your body for that matter. I still feel the touch of your satin smooth baby like skin if I concentrate very hard. But I doubt if I'll ever feel skin that soft again.

How did I feel that night? I venture to say potent for a one word answer. I really thought when I was getting undressed that when you dropped out of your gown in your natural state I would pop a giant wad of sperm all over your clean sheets. Of course that wasn't the case. In fact I was quite amazed that you could fondle me, suck me and even fuck me without my coming instantly. That made me feel really good, because I knew that I would be able to please you a lot longer before becoming A.F.O. (ALL FUCKFD OUT). I thought I was controlling my ejaculation extremely well. I think I could have actually stayed in you all night or at least a good part of it without coming, so that I could give you lots of orgasms. I could feel you come a few times the last times we fucked. That felt dynamite. But that wasn't the best part. I was never so aroused in my life when you started moaning with that sensuous voice of yours . . . "fuck me, fuck me, give it to me. Put it in deeper." I could feel my hardon dying just before that. All those erotic little moans of yours really do the trick. That filled me so full of passion that I couldn't help myself from going completely animal in you. I couldn't have gone any faster or deeper into you than in those precious moments. I just wanted to give you such a tremendous orgasm that I thought that I was going to bury you in the mattress forever. My cock just wanted to pound your vagina to shreds and make you come like you never did before. I think that the only thing that saved you from total oblivion was my orgasm. It is amazing to me that a simple, well not so simple, yet quick thing like an orgasm can save a guy from a sex crazed monster to a content gentle sleepy lump a few seconds later. That's good in a way I guess. But once a guy comes that is it for now anyway. He has to start building up from scratch all over again. Unless he's got a cock like Samson and the horneyness to match. You women you're lucky. You get aroused and you come and come and come and come and come till you practically die of pleasure. (What a wonderful way to die). You really have the good end of sex I think. You feel the total sensation of a giant cock blasting away savagely against the sensitive walls of your vagina with such power and force. If you harnassed it you could sell it to Con Edison to light the city. If one guy gets tired, you can get another one just as anxious to illuminate you as the first guy. You could practically go on and on like this forever, or at least until your body is pooped. And that is highly improbable in your particular case.

That is not all. You even have a choise of where to put the cock. If you get tired of the conventional way you can suck on it and greek it. In fact, although I may be wrong, it might be possible to do all three at once. Have you ever tried that? Just think, if you had an orgasm from each one at the same time.

Let's get away from cocks for a second. A woman has tits, big ones much bigger of course than a man's. The sensuous woman (you) must get a great deal of pleasure from a man sucking lovingly on those sensitive breasts. She not only receives physical pleasure I think but a greater inner gratification in that it fulfills the symbolism of her maternal instincts, she is—nursing a child. A woman is also generally the receiver, while the man does his utmost to give it to a woman. Okay, sure so it works both ways, but since the man is naturally the aggressor the woman just has to feel that. Well, that's how I feel anyway.

I'm not knocking my male sexuality. It's fun from my side of the fence too. You can bet your sweet, chubby little ass it is. I would love to stick my tongue into that beautiful vagina of yours and explore that soft heavenly area for hours and make you come again and again. I felt that when I was eating your pussy, Xaviera, that somehow I was in the most utterly secure cozyest place in the world. I just loved eating you, after I got over my shyness in doing it I wanted to stay there forever. If that wasn't enough that death grip scissor lock you put around my head while I was down there was certainly the greatest. I loved it so much that I can't describe it any further.

There was only one thing that wasn't perfect and that was not really your fault—the feminine hygiene spray was just a mite too strong for me. There wasn't much air to breath down there and breathing fast is of course unavoidable during sex. The air must be breathable. Now I know that it is a better scent than a raunchy, smelly odor. I would be the first one to agree on that but I found that it (FDS?) just too overwhelming for eating you with any great deal of zeal. Although your vagina is super clean without that stuff. I read an article in CONSUMER REPORT recently and I think you should have the benefit of reading it too, you may or may not agree with it, but they're usually pretty accurate and objective. Please read it for me and tell me what you think of it. You are definitely the cleanest, not to mention the most sensuous woman in the world. It takes no stroke of genius to make that observation. I just want to help you become even better. In my next letter I'll send you an article on what many

68

doctors consider to be the feminine fountain of youth. Maybe I'll even send you some of the fountain itself, to get you started. I just want you to stay looking young and pretty for many years to come, as I know you certainly do after what you've done for me that is the very least I can do. You are truly among the nicest woman in the whole world Xaviera. I say that with sincerety. You love everybody and I think just about everybody loves you. I do at least.

Love and many, many kisses.

Your Phil

Well, to say the least, I was entertained and amused by Phil's terribly enthusiastic letter, and was glad he'd gotten some flattering attention from his friends as a result of our evening together. So I answered him a few days after receiving his letter.

Dear Phil:

Thank you very much for your letter which you sent directly to Amsterdam. I'm happy to know that not only did I enjoy myself tremendously, but you did as well. I'd like to hear more about your new adventures if you have any and how you like being a man and not a boy anymore. Also, how you like seducing girls and whether or not you've been rejected. I'm sure you haven't been but write me about it.

Also I must agree about the feminine hygiene spray and indeed it was FDS. I have refrained from using it even before I received your letter because it doesn't seem to be healthy and I now stick to nice body lotions and lemon-smelling powders to make me fragrant. I do know that I'm clean, squeaky clean as you may call it. You know I like to smell nice and I always thought that feminine spray would taste nice. I didn't realize that it

69

would be difficult to inhale. Sorry about that, but after breathing the odor of the feminine spray, you **did** get turned on tremendously and you did say in your letter that you enjoyed every bit of our time together.

In Europe, I must say, the hygienic customs are slightly different. I'm so used to douching and taking a bath, twice, three times a day sometimes that it's amazing to see how little the Dutch women take care of themselves—and the Dutchmen as well—so far as their own cleanliness is concerned. Douching here is out of the question. The women say that it is bad for you and that it will prevent them from getting female diseases if they don't douche—that is, the more you douche, the less resistance you have. For this theory I'd have to check with a doctor and find out if this has been proven medically. However, I'm so used to being clean inside as well as out that perhaps I shouldn't overdo it and just take a good bath once a day and just douche once instead of two or three times. But these all are female problems which I'm sure you're not too interested in.

Hopefully, someday I'll be back in the U.S. and I've got your phone number and I'll call you and when you make love to me, I want you to be the aggressor. You said in your letter that men are supposed to be the aggressor, so I will let you do all the work and seduce me. It will make me feel like a little girl again.

Goodbye, Phil, and good luck.

Xaviera

Dear Xaviera,

Hi there, you sexy, beautiful creature!

How's things over there? In fact, where the hell are you? I hope you got my other letters. I guess you're very busy (as usual).

I am, too. I'm working at a country club, where I serve refreshments. My place is at the golf course—the members stop there to grab something. Speaking of grabbing something—sometimes I get these young girls who come over from the pool to get something to eat. One time I was serving them these huge hot dogs we have. As I was taking one out of the pan with my pincers, it was rocking back and forth, or rather I should say I was wiggling it back and forth. I knew the girls were watching me and finally they started giggling out loud. I knew they would. I'd like to wiggle my dick in between their juicy legs.

There are two cute-looking girls about my own age who work here. One is Edith, a tall slim blonde who has great eyes, a lovely complexion and a nice warm personality. I hope to get to know her better by the end of summer. Then there is Rachel, whose face isn't as nice as Edith's, but she's got a sexier body, with huge breasts, which I'm dying to suck on! Maybe . . . maybe . . . maybe. . . .

I took a girl named Judith to a Met game last week and we had a good time, even though the Mets lost. I wouldn't mention this except that it was my first date ever!

I have to laugh at that. Here I am, 19 years old, going out for the first time with a girl after getting laid! I bet not too many guys have done that. I want to ask her out at least one more time.

You know, Xaviera, after you screwed me, I didn't feel like jerking off for over two weeks, but one day I felt the urge to have an orgasm so badly that while I was taking a shower I started rubbing my cock and when I came, it felt so good that I almost fainted from sheer pleasure.

My sperm never shot so far before, either, and tons of it came out, which made the whole experience even more exhilerating. It seems that the more sperm you ejaculate, the better quality orgasm you have. That one felt super!

From now on, I'm not going to jerk off like I used to—constantly until my balls start aching. I'll wait for a good time.

Of course I can't stop completely. Well, actually it's because I don't want to stop. Why miss out on the pleasure of coming, so long as you don't hurt yourself or your fucking? Of course if I could fuck as often as I want to, I probably wouldn't jerk off any more. Fucking (you anyway) is totally *super!* There's just nothing like it, and I love it.

71

I hope I can get intimate with one of these girls, hopefully one that digs fucking the way it should—the way *you* do.

If I get a "live one," I'll be sure to write and tell you about it. I just sent away for 3 dozen fetherlite condoms from a population planning outfit in North Carolina. These English rubbers are the best—$3.50 a dozen. They're super-light, clear and lubricated—you can hardly tell you're wearing it.

Of course I'd rather fuck without one, but the girl's protection is the most important thing, not to mention V.D., which is rampant here. It can't (using a rubber) be that bad, although I have a friend who once said, "fucking with a rubber is like taking a shower with your raincoat on." I have a feeling he's right. However, what must be must be. Girls must be protected.

Xaviera, could you please write to me soon here at my new P.O. Box (for my rubbers and other assorted goodies). I'd like to get one of those vibrating dildos, but I don't feel like sending my money to one of those sleazy outfits in California. Do you know where I could get one?

Well, I guess I'll say goodbye for now. When will you come back here? When is your book coming out? I'm dying to see it!

Love & tender Frenches,

Phil

P.S. One of my friends asked me if you ever balled Henry Kissinger? I said that you wouldn't fuck for an ugly jerk like that. Well?

(Editors' Note: This letter was written in November 1972.)

Dear Xaviera,

Hi! Thanks for remembering me.

It's taken me a thousand phone calls to find out where you are, and your last letter had no address. If I'd known you were in Canada for so long, I'd had written you there.

I've been writing to a girl I met last summer and in a recent letter, I told her about you and me. I felt as though I should tell her sooner or later, just to see how she reacted. I'm sure how she reacted 'cause she hasn't written to me in a while. She goes to Antioch and does very well there. She's the first girl I've known that is smart, cute, and is a real nice kid.

She doesn't have any nasty habits, either. I was surprised when she wrote me and told me that I was the *first* boy ever to ask her out! She said she really flipped when I did, too.

I'd love her to meet you sometime, Xaviera. I'm sure she'd feel the same way, too.

Hey, finally found a really good article on Vitamin E. Please read it. I guarantee you'll be taking 2,000 units a day like Jimmy Brown and that actress. I ran down to the drugstore myself and bought a big bottle of 400 unit capsules.

They really do make *me* feel sexier. I think they'll really help you stay young-looking as well.

Well, Xaviera, that's about all I have to say right now. I'd sure like to suck on some pussy! Sometimes I feel so horny!

I hope you will write me once in a while.

> Hope to see you soon.
>
> I love you!
>
> Phil

*   *   *

That was the last I've heard from Phil. I guess I owe him a letter.

Dear Xaviera,

I am lying here in bed with your latest book sitting on my nightstand. I just finished it and thought I'd drop you a few lines in hopes that you will receive them.

You are an absolute god send my dear, a real love. You tell it like it is and mince no words. I find this so refreshing today when so much is "beat around" the proverbial bush.

Even though I haven't met you, I feel very close to you. I've followed your life quite closely, guess you might say your one of my idol personalities, *truthfully*. Your books really bring back memories of my "hooking days." (I feel a little explanation should be made here. I'm Jonathan Barlow, 23, gay, quite astoundingly handsome and a vet-ran hooker.)

Like you I found I had to quit because of the law etc, but I still manage quite nicely. I'd been hooking for 4 years prior to my 21st birthday, so I feel I know of what you speak. We also come from practically the same back-grounds so I feel a type of sister-brother relationship there.

I guess what I really wanted to say is thanks for saying what others haven't been able to. I remain forever en-debted—

Jonathan Barlow

Martha's Vineyard, Mass.

Dear Ms. Hollander:

I sincerely found your book an entertaining and enlightening reading experience. For me, at least, the most amusing section was your breakdown of lovers according to their ethnic backgrounds. I must say that my own experience in no way concurs with yours, but will defer to you because of your far wider range of experience. I also must say I envy you that!

On the matter of my government's actions with regard to you—once again it is being demonstrated that this nation has a strange (perverted) sense of values. We sanction murders (political assassinations, and war itself) at the same time we abhor and chastise prostitution. I can only, as one American citizen who is embarrassed—and angered—by her country's performance in this area of morality, apologize to you and offer the explanation that America has a great deal of growing up to do.

I cannot see a single thing wrong with what you have been doing. If it is in any way a "crime," it is a victimless crime. More significant, however, is what seems manifestly obvious to me—that the most important thing a person can do in life is to be honest and not knowingly try to hurt other people. Judging by your book, at least, you certainly qualify in these areas and it's just one more piece of hypocrisy for our system to punish you. Hopefully, one day America will grow up a bit and attain a measure of realistic values.

Until that time, I hope you can be happy in whatever endeavor you may wish to try or whatever field you choose to enter. Actually, I envy you your return to Europe—though not the circumstances of your leaving America!—because I wish I were still living there. I find the European style of living to be far more relaxing and certainly much more humane than our presently constituted American one.

In any event, my very best wishes for your future and if you should happen to find the time to comment on my letter, your reply will be most welcome.

Cordially,

Lucretia MacDonald

Hastings-on-Hudson, New York

Dear Sirs,
The Story "The Happy Hooker" Xaviera Hollander, is —indeed Par-Excellent. Brief, to the Point. Human, "To Err is Human, to Forgive Divine", such as writer Learned

at age 7 yrs. in Ireland in village of about 50 persons all told 1-Priest, 1-Minister both of sermons. That "Fire & Brimstone, Plus Hell Fire in Ever-Lasting Torment. Plus. If one could Read the 10 Commandments, the Last *10* were read by Minister and by Priest of Catholic Church Time 1880. The answer by Sexton & Congregation was & Still is "Lord have Mercy—upon us and *Incline* our Hearts to Keep this Law "Amen The World to Day Believes Words, Lawyers too." *INCLINE* as way out, Cardinal Newman, formerly Church of England says—Largeness of Mind, Abbhorence of Strife, Clemency, of Britizism, Absence of Suspicion, Tenderness of Compassion, *LOVE* of ALL Mankind. Be unto us A Tower of Strength —and a Fount of Consolation Now, and in the days of Account, Amen.

Miss Xaviera Hollander is, I believe a *TYPE,* "Mental Muscular Person" means one who does. Put Muscular Action Thru Mental Ideas. This is an Executive Number-1 in Profession of "Ladies of the Evening." Yet, as stated in Book "British are Cold." not so. If Xaviera used her "Slow Heating Ideas" would bring *HEAT*—That Xaviera would *Please* Bring an ASBESTOS Extinguisher. Pronto. Amen.

However, XAVIERA has—IT—*not* Goodness, *Not Badness.*—or *ANY* Virtues. Just am that what I am. Oh Love Divine Do Not Let Me Go. Let Me Rest My Weary Head in Thee, Amen. XAVIERA *You* are A Darling of Nature, So True, So Sincere. *Love* Rules The World anyway—XAVIERA, You Know. *Wars.* Today & 1914-1918. *Result,* Negative—*Love,* Positive. This writer spoke to a lovely woman in St. Mihiel near Verdun France October 1918. That Crown Prince Wilhelm of Germany *Paid in Gold for Love* (as German Money had no Value, They Lost the War) *amen.* The German Soldiers from 1914-1918 left many children in France. this writer saw them. Their Heads were German, on *"Fine la Guere."* This Young woman showed War Weariness. Brought her RIGHT HAND to her Throat said *we women* will Kill

76

them as & when Armistice is Signed. The women Dug a Large Hole On Early Morning as War was to cease, November 11th, 1918 they cut the Germans (Huns) throats. All Buried *no Regrets*. The Government Returned to Paris with the then President of the French Republic M. POINCARE—who Declared that is Now Lawful to Detroy children of German Soldiers of Kaiser's Armies. Remember "Earth Hath No Sorrows that Heaven Cannot Heal." XAVIERA. *You* are so Right, *a real* woman You Make your Gracious Ways, Very Catching. Lovely. You are an Angel from The Land of Love. Showers of Blessings Allways to You, So So *Real* So Human. *Yes*. This Writer that Houses of *Love* Be made convenient in U.S.A. so V.D. will end—*Note,* Spain, Portugal, have Licensed Houses and these *2* nations are Catholic. *No* Objections by Church or State. Right. Result: No Venereal Diseases. Now an Ounce of Prevention is Worth a Pound of Cure. Good luck to You XAVIER Allways. Am War I Soldier, Saw Service in Germany too. Not young. But Alive 1972. Age 4-Score and more. Cheerio.

Alvin T. Rogers

U. S. Army, Ret.

Little Neck, N.Y.

Dear Miss Hollander:

I just finished your book which I found very great, educational, and enlightening. I would be very pleased if you could send me an autographed picture of yourself, which I would be very grateful for.

Also, if you wouldn't mind, I write to many famous people as pen pals, and receive letters from them all the time. So if you could find the time I'd like to hear from you occasionally.

My name is Mickey Fischer, I'm 24 years old, manage a

Records Department in a store, Hobbies are Photography
and playing my Bass Guitar.

                                        Thank you,

                                        Mickey Fischer
                                        The Bronx, N.Y.

Dear Miss Hollander,
   Undoubtably, you must receive a lot of mail; probably
too much to bother with answering each letter. Or even
any letter. At least I hope you are still enthusiastic enough
to *read* your mail, if not answer it.
   I'm going to try to keep this as short as I can, Miss Hollander. I may as well introduce myself by telling you the
worst; I am a 31-year-old convict serving a life sentence
for murder. I have served ten years of my sentence. I was
20 when I was first sentenced.
   A while ago I had a chance to read some of your book,
"The Happy Hooker." I wish now that I knew you a little
better—I wish I knew you at all! I don't know you at all,
of course, except through your book. And as I said, I
didn't even read all of that. Poor me!
   To get back to all of the letters you've been receiving.
Perhaps many of them were indignant, perhaps others
were angry ones, and some small percentage, no doubt,
were crank letters. Nutty. Crazy. Weird.
   This letter might be nutty, crazy, and weird. However,
Miss Hollander, it is *not* a crank letter. It has taken me a
long time to write this. Even now the words might not be
adequate, or you may misunderstand my intention, or you
may totally ignore this. But if I don't write this letter now,
I'll probably never write it at all. I'm scared that your
reaction to this will be one of two extremes: you'll either
laugh yourself sick (which would be humiliating for me to
know), or you'll become very angry (which to me would
be just as undesireable as if you laughed).

But, I cannot write something like this to Dear Abby

Like many cons I know, you've been around, Miss Hollander. And judging from the tone of your book, you haven't become hardened by life . . . by your life. And I know that people like you and I, who have been through the baser things in life, are better able than most to know and understand the noble aspects of life, too. We've both seen people at their very worst, as well as at their very best. We've seen the wickedness that exists in good men, but, perhaps more importantly, we've seen also the goodness that lives in wicked men. After a life like that, after all the hard lessons, one begins to become less judgemental, less prejudiced.

Now, don't laugh, because I'm utterly serious, Miss Hollander. At the time I entered prison, I had never had sexual intercourse with a woman (or with a man either, for that matter). I didn't worry too much about being "cherry" at 20—I mean, I knew it wouldn't last much longer! But—I ended up in prison. For life.

In 1962, I know that I couldn't have been the only 20-year-old kid in America who had never slept with a woman. But *now* it is 1972. *Now* I am 31-years-old. In my prison years I haven't turned to men but, as you know, women are not very available in adult male "correctional institutions."

Which is no particular problem if I spend the rest of my life here. I mean, who would ever know?

But there is hope that I may be released sometime soon. And, Miss Hollander, *I* have a problem! I could always visit a whorehouse or something, I suppose. *If* I get out. The only catch is that it's been ten years since I've walked down a street. Miss Hollander, I couldn't even *find* a bordello! And if I did, how would I know how clean it was? And I'd have to explain things, too, or else my partner wouldn't know what to think when a full-grown adult didn't know what to. . . . well, what to *do!* Disastrous, huh?!!!

(Gee, I hope you've read this far, Miss Hollander. This is sounding more and more like a crank letter to *me,* never mind what *you* are going to think!)

Have I convinced you, Miss Hollander, that I am not a depraved madman? At least, if I *am* depraved, I've used it to my best advantage. Maybe my depravity is more normal than other depravities . . . I don't know.

I know that I have a good chance at a successful life. However, I am also the world's *only* 31-year-old virgin, of *either* sex! That might be some accomplishment, but it isn't something one can shout from every rooftop, you know? What ego value is there in an accomplishment you have to keep a secret??

Look, I'm not trying to set up a tryst with you, or anything like that. What I *would* like, though, is an opportunity to correspond with you. Maybe I am too hung-up and concerned about this whole sex thing, but still, maybe you could give me advice as to what to do, how best to handle this situation once I'm out, or maybe just provide a listening ear. You could certainly judge whether or not my concerns and worries and fears are real or not. Maybe they are just concerns and worries and fears that every normal depraved person has. I have no way to judge and, as you can imagine, it is very much on my mind.

I know this is very presumptious of me, Miss Hollander, but you can always tear this up and throw it away. You just might do that. And if you did, I'd understand. If I got a letter this bizarre, I'm not sure what my reaction would be! But I would be very, very grateful to you if you could be of help to me—just via letters.

As I said earlier, I cannot write a letter like this to Dear Abby, nor can I contact the Office of Emergency Preparedness (don't they handle disasters?), or the like. Doc Kinsey is dead, too. And the cell block officer wouldn't be much help either—he's a fag. And all the books assume one has a partner handy to practice with in a sort of "on-the-job" training! And I definitely cannot talk to my mother about this, as she might report it and then how would I ever explain *that* to the parole board????! That's a no-no.

I hope I'll be fortunate enough to hear from you. Thank you for reading this far, Miss Hollander.

Sincerely,

Victor Elias Brown

Joliet, Ill.

PS: Incoming and outgoing mail is not censored, Miss Hollander, in case you were concerned that someone else, a prison censor, actually *read* this! No, no one else has read it, so don't fear on that score.

If you haven't taken this seriously, or if you think I'm a weirdo, all I ask is that you tear it up and throw it away.

Hello—

I guess this might be called a fan letter, though I cringe at that particular term. My only excuse for writing you a letter is that I would like to get to know you, if only through correspondence. I have read your book and heard your statement on the radio about advocation of a pleasure house staffed by young men for women. A rather intriguing idea. Are there any such places already in existence?

As for an introduction, I am 25 years old, tall, large-boned and I recently shaved off a beautiful red beard because I am training for personnel service in the airlines business. However, I have retained a mustache. I'm a pipe and cigar smoker and am generally serious and given to silences before speaking. Presently I'm employed by a firm dealing in remaindered books, where the pay is next to nothing.

I live alone with about seven hundred books, a radio, a TV and a typewriter. Making it as a writer is that Ultimate

Goal behind all the scramble to make a little money in the interim. And some day I will make my home in beautiful upstate New Hampshire.

If you have the time, I am interested in a reply.

Cordially,

Harold Dawes
Atlanta, Ga.

Dear Xaviera,

Loved yr. book.

I am 23 years old and married with one child. My marriage would be fine except for two things.

First I always seem to reach an orgasim before my wife and this has caused many problems between us. I always seem to have an orgasim when I can tell she is begining to get her rocks off. This leaves her in deep heat, emotionally spent and usually mad because I left her dangling again. Is there anything I can do to keep from reaching an orgasim until she does?

Second is that my wife doesn't beleive in fellating, cunniling, or oral sex in any way. We have had cunnilings before and she enjoyed it immensely but it takes everything in my power to get her to let me do it to her again. She likes it but she thinks its wrong. Is there some way that might help me to convince her to remove her inhibitations?

Also could these be connected in any way?

Thanks in advance,

Edgar Glenville
Pocatello, Idaho

Dear Madame Xaviera,

Your book gave me a big pleasure—though I am of another kind of people—an old Russian emigrant, educated in spirit of XIX century Romantics. Dear Madame, your book cannot be called pornographic—it is rather in spirit of XVIII century. And your person is wonderful, all you say—is perfectly right. Also it is a document of vast human tragedy—I had one like that as young girl—and then—I took men as a bitter pill—but necessary for health.

The more modest circumstances of my life didn't permit me much in this sense—an emigrant's life is struggle for existence—very hard. But I follow your spirit, even in question of homosexuality. When I was a little girl—I had the worst shock of my life when I understood that love is rather for man and woman, not for two women. Look at animals—they follow nature only—can it be unnatural? But I saw the same homosexual activities between animals, so are they unnatural?

You are the last of Greek hetaerae, you did read "Aphrodite" (I forgot the name of author)? And so—my dear and wonderful girl I wish you good luck and don't sell your rich personality for a billy goat—I mean husband, kids and kitchen pleasures.

Yours very truly,

Dounia Borodine

Harvard University

Cambridge, Mass.

Dear Miss Hollander:

Your "Happy Hooker" was a very interesting piece of literature. Through it you have presented yourself as an interesting personality.

I am a student at Schoolcraft Community College, Livonia, Michigan, and introduced your book to my English class—the response was good.

It was this response that prompted me to go to Mr. Patrick Neuman, our activities director. At this point we're scheduling lectures for the 1972-73 school year. Mr. Neuman, who was familiar with your book, assured me you would have a warm welcome at our school.

As a member of the activities committee I ask you, should time permit, to lecture at our school somewhere between September and April.

Again, let me say that we are now in the midst of scheduling for fall and winter. Your answer within the next two weeks would be appreciated.

Miss Hollander, I sincerely feel your visit would be informative, witty and interesting to all of us. Please come visit our school.

Best regards,

Anna Otzelnais
Livonia, Michigan

Dear Miss Hollander,

I got a lot of laughs out of your book at the beginning, but then had to force myself to finish it. I suspect you began by telling the truth, and then got carried away. Anyway, I tossed it aside as the latest piece of tripe (like "The Sensuous Woman") trying to cash in on the porno market.

To my amazement, it became a best seller. It's the first "dirty" book I've seen people reading openly on the subways. (Usually, they cover them in plain brown wrappers.)

As a non-American, someone should tell you that we are still a very sexually inhibited country. I think more than anything that explains the success of your book. Also it has a quality of "sincerity" that the other filthy books don't have. Hang onto that quality; it's the reason you've

84

had two best sellers in a row. It's your caviar and crackers.

I've been working on a novel for 15 years, so you can understand my resentment and jealousy of you who has succeeded so quickly with such a lightweight book. But don't lose that "sincere" quality or you will wind up just like all the others; an also-ran in the pseudo-pornographic race.

If you really want to do something unusual, you might subsidize me for the next two years, when I'll have completed my elephantine book. I can live on about $3,000 a year, so $6,000 should do it.

Think of the great publicity for you.

Sincerely,

Ben di Brienzi
Brooklyn, N.Y.

Dear Miss Hollander:
I am a normally horny guy, 27 years old, who hasn't fucked one girl so far in my life. It's almost unbelievable. In all these years I haven't even gotten my hands under a girl's blouse or skirt. What I means is that I've never touched a girl's cunt or boobs.

Well, it's sure not because I lack interest in the opposite sex. O wow, I'm horny all the time. I get a quick erection even if I see a bra in a store window. One day I was in the local department store and got a strong erection when I went by the panties counter.

As you might imagine, I masturbate like crazy. Two times a day isn't uncommon for me. At least it relieves the tension that comes from being so passionate all the time.

I would give so much to fuck a girl—my poor cock just aches for a moist, warm cunt.

What should I do? How can I find someone to fuck or get fucked by me?

Another thing—my erection is only about five-and-a-half inches—what can I do to make it real big—like seven or eight inches? Are there exercises I can do?

I wish I could screw you, suck your breasts and clitoris and put my finger in your ass hole. Will you permit me?

Kind of desperate,

Neil Warren Underhill

Provo, Utah

Dear Miss Hollander;

Beautiful lady, I hope that you will consider this a compliment as what I am doing is completely out of my Scorpio character.

I read your book and I found it to be quite marvelous. Your book indicates that your beauty is to be exceeded only by your charm. When you combine sincere warmth and complete honesty with these qualities you have a very rare and beautiful person.

If your intention was, as you said, to put a different light on the professional prostitute, you certainly succeeded. However, I doubt that all of them possess the qualities that you have.

For me, writing this letter is exceptional. As presumptuous as it may seem, had we met I'm sure we could have been friends. Please don't misunderstand me. I'm not a swinger. I just happen to groove on attractive people who are intelligent, warm and sincere.

If I read you right, you will enjoy this poem I copied out of an old English anthology when I was a girl. I've forgotten who the author is.

Time is . . .
Too slow for those who wait,

86

Too swift for those who fear,
Too long for those who grieve,
Too short for those who rejoice,
But for those who love, Time is eternity.

I hope that you find long and lasting happiness, as you are truly one of the beautiful people.

Again, I don't mean to be presumptuous but my address is [deleted] just in case you run into one of those lonely nights. I would be flattered to see you use it.

With warmest regards,

Ina Claire Bryce
White River Junction, N.Y.

Dear Xaviera,

I hope I'm not being forward, but I feel the only way to contact you is to be nice 'n direct.

I'm 46 and long married and bored unto death with my wife. If I were to guess at the truth, it's probably the same story at her end. But I gave up long ago hoping that we'd ever overcome the humdrum, wham-bang dumb sex life we have. I mean, I frankly think we screw because you're supposed to when you're married.

Can't I come to town some time, wine 'n dine you, and—to be frank and, I guess, dirty-mouthed, at the same time—fuck your eyes out? I don't mean for pay because I know you're out of that. But I'd spring for a great dinner —have you ever been to The Copain, the First Avenue place where part of "The French Connection" was filmed? —and do the town before retiring to my hotel suite. I always stay at one of the best hotels in the city, so you wouldn't be ashamed to go home with me.

I think you like challenge, Xaviera, and my challenge to

you is—make me see stars! I'll do my best to do the same to you!

Yours, hopefully,

Henry C. Muller
Houston, Texas

Dear Madame Hollander:
We four Hookers have just finished reading your book and we would like to tell you that we did not believe a word of it.
We have had experience in many sex activities and have found it impossible (humanly impossible) to believe that all this happened to one person.
In conclusion, we are stating our professional opinions that your experiences ocurred in such sequence they are hard to believe.
All of these things happening to one person? Come on now, who are you kidding?
Some people will say anything to make a buck!!!!

Four Prosperous Prostitutes,

Frances, Ursula, Carol and Katherine
Chicago, Ill.

Dear Ms. Hollander,
Being an established perennial bachelor, I have read quite a few books on the subject you write of.
I think your book is quite entertaining. It even tops Virginia McManus's "Not for Love," although you have to remember that in those days you couldn't say as much.
Is your book in the libraries? That would really be a

piece of progress of landmark dimensions. I remember being in an older friend's library and finding a whole shelf of Olympia Press editions—Henry Miller and the rest—and at the same time I could hear his red-haired wife splashing in the shower. My 19 years of age cried out for sustenance.

I guess one could fall in love with a lady of the evening. They turn you down 25 years ago and you still see them plying their trade 25 years later. I once knew a place that looked like a Hollywood setting and featured only Jewish girls. Thereby destroying one myth. . . .

Women have been trying to outwit me since kindergarten. I don't know why. All they have to do is say, "Give me some money."

Your ardent reader,

Manfred Brenton

Point-of-Woods

Fire Island

New York

Dear Miss Hollander:

I really enjoyed your book. It showed your very liberal.

I have a problem I'd like to talk over with you if you don't mind. It's kind of delicate, but I know you'll understand.

I only like two kinds of women, and God Help Me, there's no logic in it: I love pregnant ladies, and I like dominant ladies. With a pregnant lady who isn't too far gone, I can have two-three orgasms in one hour. With a dominant lady, I like to give her pleasure but I still manage my two-three orgasms per hour.

I'm not into any fetishes—leather or any of that shit—but the above is a constant concern of mine.

Do you have any advice for me?

Cordially,

Ben McFarland

El Paso, Texas

Dear Xaviera,

I am writing you because your book, "The Happy Hooker," convinces me that you are an understanding human being: a *"mensche."*

In an age of liberal ideas, I was raised in a conservative household. We were taught to suppress our sexual desires. My younger brother Marvin rebelled and at 16 is already experimenting with sex. I, the oldest brother at 19, am all uptight about the whole subject.

The typical dates I have had could only be described as platonic at best, all with *gute Yiddische Maidlach,* sweet as sugar on the outside and cold as fish on the inside. Since I am human, though, I need an outlet. Going out with them makes me feel physically like a virtual monk. I don't want to be screwed up sexually the rest of my life because of severe early training.

To get to the point, whorish girls always turn me off immediately, that's why I dated all the goodie two-shoes types. I now feel that maybe someone in your profession could help me.

I guess I could ask one of my uncles for the address of a bordello, but they are just as strait-laced as my parents. I would greatly appreciate it if you could send me the address of one of your colleagues in Manhattan.

As a college student I could only afford about $20 if I scrimped and saved. Maybe Inez could help me (she's mentioned in your book and she seems very sympathetic).

It may not be relevant, but I am 5 feet 10, 183 lbs, with green eyes and dark hair. I have an average build and am better than average looking. Urges for homosexual or "kinky" relationships have siezed me extremely rarely. All I really want is an experience which is natural and, well, beautiful, I guess.

I write you as a fellow Jew who needs professional assistance. A speedy answer would be greatly appreciated, more than you will ever know. You'll always have my personal admiration.

Sincerely—and *Shalom*

Aviva Leontovich

Stamford, Conn.

P.S. Please don't feel that I am ashamed of our correspondence. But when you write to me, please use your initials instead of your full name. My family is very narrowminded on the subject of sex.

Dear Miss Hollander,

Your book has been an eye-opener for a lot of people. I lent it to my own widowed mother (she's 60) and now she's all for legalizing prostitution! This is quite an accomplishment as she is very conservative toward sex.

I am 23 years old, married since I was 19 and last year learned the joys of bisexuality. My husband and I are both great fans of yours. So is my girl friend, who is also my husband's girl friend. Or I should say *was*, as a demon called jealousy stepped in for a while and they're turning up their noses at each other. But things are still great between my girl friend and I—never better. She's been with us more than a year now, sort of a three-way marriage type thing, you know? Well, maybe if we get a bigger bed they'll make up. Anyway, we'll be needing one for parties, if you know what I mean. Maybe you'd like to join us sometime.

I'd like to start an Xaviera Hollander fan club and would like your advice on how to go about it.

Lots of luck in all your enterprises.

Got eyes for you,

Mrs. Cleo Bunker

Durham, Conn.

Dear Miss Hollander:

I have just finished reading your book and I would like to share some thoughts of my own with you. From the letterhead on my stationery, you can see that I am in Christian work, and you are probably expecting condemnation from me, but this is not the case. I ask you, out of courtesy, to at least hear me out before you decide that you are definitely not interested.

To begin with, I want you to know how much Jesus loves you. I don't know if anyone has ever told you this or not, and what a tragedy it would be if you lived your entire life without learning that fact. Probably you have been exposed to many forms of "religion," but that is not what I am talking about. And, like many of us, you may be fed up with all the hypocrisy you see around you from so-called Christians or "moral" people. What I am talking about, however, is an exciting, vibrant, secure relationship with the Man, Jesus Christ, who died on the cross for your sins and mine, and who came back from the grave to give us eternal life.

You may say that you don't have conviction for your sins, but your own words in your book betray you. You show a very distinct awareness of right and wrong; there are many instances of standards of conduct in your own life. When you accused the police and others of persecuting you, you are reflecting a basic criterion for human rights and privileges. Where does this criterion come from? It comes from your conscience, which God has placed inside you to guide you.

So, even though the Bible says that we have all sinned (Romans 3:23), God loved us so much that he sent his own son to die for us, to take our sin upon himself so that we wouldn't have to suffer the penalty—which is eternal separation from God. I don't know what hell is like, but I know that I don't want to go there because God is not there. When God is absent, there can only be darkness, despair and perversion, and most of all, bitter loneliness.

You stated in the last pages of your book that you supposed that there would "always be new opportunities for an ambitious, active Dutch girl to be happy and give pleasure to others." This is not true. Prostitution will go on, I'm sure, but you will not necessarily be part of it, nor will you be happy. You are young and attractive now, but you will not always have your youth and beauty. You may have intelligence, money, prestige, friends and beauty, but these things will not satisfy you ultimately. Sooner or later you are going to realize that the *only* thing worthwhile is your personal relationship with God.

I am not denying that sin is pleasurable, for it is, but "only for a season," as the Bible states. It is also obvious that you have tried to justify yourself by giving some happiness along with your body, by filling a "lost hour of loneliness by giving them a warm smile, a cold drink, soft music in the background, and then a warm and young body to hold, to press, to kiss, to make love to." Is this indeed a sin? you say. Yes, indeed, it is. You are only one more of the millions of victims that Satan has been deceiving since time began. There is *nothing* wrong with sex, for God created it, but Satan takes the good gifts of God and perverts them. The misuse of sex is what makes it wrong. Satan has so perverted you, dear lady, and jaded your conscience to such an extent that you can never get out of this trap alone. Only Jesus can wipe away the sin and the guilt and give you a new life.

In my work, I have dealt with people from every walk of life. I spent four years on Sunset Strip in Hollywood, and met prostitutes, junkies, homosexuals, businessmen, movie stars, millionaires, etc. I'm doing the same kind of work here. I have seen countless numbers try to escape the hell of their lives through drugs, liquor, sex and suicide. No matter how big the smile on the outside, *every one* of us is looking for love, acceptance, security, and this is just not possible except through the love of Jesus. You may think you are happy now, but I promise you that this will not last. I beg you, dear, precious girl, to begin to take inventory of your life and open your heart to Jesus before it is too late. I have seen girls in your profession do this, and how Christ has completely changed them. God has given you so much, Xaviera. Why not honor him with it, rather than rebelling against him? He loves you so much.

You may only laugh as you read this, or you may not read it at all, but some day God is going to remind you of it. He is going to say, "Xaviera, you were warned. You have no excuse." *I* am not saying this. God says it in his word. Jesus makes it very plain that "He that believes on Him is not judged; but he who does not believe is judged already. He has already been convicted; has already received his sentence because he has not believed on and trusted in the name of the only begotten Son of God—He is condemned for refusing to let his trust rest in Christ's name." (John 3:18)

I am going to pray for you every day, and I want you to know that I will always be available to talk with you or write to you if you ever want to contact me. Never forget how much Jesus loves you, and I love you because He has permitted me to see you with His eyes.

In Christ,

Roberta Fabricant
Director

Seminary for Wayward Girls,

Racine, Wisconsin

94

Dear Miss Hollander,

We, the residents of the Third Floor, South Wing of Joseph R. Pearson Hall at the University of Kansas, request your presence for the soul purpose of enlightening us in the ever present, ever-discussed topic of sex! After reading your book, which, by the way, was beautifully done, we here at Lawrence are all convinced that you are the most knowledgable woman on the topic at hand. We are interested in acquiring your services for a week-end at your convenience.

Due to the fact that we are all students, we cannot promise great financial rewards. However, we can promise the mental and physical satisfaction of "setting us straight" on a subject that is an important part of our lives, and we are sure, yours.

We wish to thank you for allowing us to present our request for your consideration, and hope that if we fail to meet, you will continue to lead a lustful and wantonly life.

Sincerely yours,

The Residents
Third Floor, South
Box 439

Lawrence, Kansas

Dear Xaviera,

Just finished reading "The Happy Hooker." It was great —great—I loved it all—

Being an artist—and an excellent one—I noticed as well as admired your front cover face. It really is fantastically expressive, and I was inspired to draw it. I don't often pick a face to draw and I have never picked one off a book cover such as I'm doing now—I draw my children each year on my Christmas card and I'd be glad to mail you one to show you I'm really serious about your face—I

95

would have copies, either the front or back cover, but your fur hat seemed distracting so if you will mail me a picture I'll draw you. Be sure the face is no smaller than the back cover if you're smiling as I must be able to detect your teeth—

There are no strings—it's just an artist inspiration sort of thing. It will be done in pencil and as I said, I'm good!

Please reply at your earliest convenience while the "mood" still lingers—

Bill Conway

Leonia, New Jersey

P.S. Excuse paper and rushed writing.

Madam,

I read your beautiful book, and would like to ask you question as expert. Could you tell me where I could read about the subject of foot fetiches? I'm not what they call a true fetichist, but I find very exciting to look or play with women's feet, specially when she's wearing nylons and shoes, not all kind of shoes, those with that thick naturel crepe rubber sole underneath. With time it becomes spongy, soft, and so marvelous to walk with. A barefooted woman excite me very much with rubbur beach sandales, then you can see her feet and toes almost sink in that spongy rubber. I also love the smell of it when it has been worn for a while, then the smell of the sandals mixt with the smell of a beautiful woman's feet. It is very exciting to me. It is enough to make me lick, suck and bit them.

Something very exciting too is a woman wearing sneakers or those thick tennis shoes with nylon stockings. The most interesting and important thing in all that matter is the way she must walk. With all that rubber and nylon, she must walk with springy way. It makes all the difference. This is a sexy walking that just a woman can do.

It is very easy to imagine then those lovely feet and toes

96

well stack in a pair of expansible nylon stockings or panty hose, the fine and well shape anckles, the calfs with it well curved design, so smooth to caress covered with nylon.

Well many men, and I'm one of them too, it is very exciting to make oral love to a woman breast around the neck or elswhere. For me one other thing which I find very exciting is to play with woman's feet. I think it's all matter of taste. Everybody has his own kicks in life, we have been raised with them and we must take the best part of it.

Charles Salant

Shreveport, La.

Dear Miss Hollander,

I have just finished reading your book and I wanted to tell you how impressed I am by your class, but more importantly, your "humaneness." You seem to really care about people, no matter who they are or what they do, and that's great! I wish the world contained more people like yourself; it then would be a much better place to live in. Thanks.

Bob Bailey

Oak Ridge, Tenn.

Dear Xaviera,

I just finished reading your book and want to say I thought it was very good, very literary. Some parts of it sound like my own life. I think you are a very beautiful and truly liberated woman, not like those phoney Fem Libbers; I admit that I look at you through bisexual eyes.

I would really appreciate it if I could have your address. I fly back and forth from Pennsylvania to Westchester in the summers. I guess I'm what the women's magazines would call a bored middle-class housewife (I'm 26) that

97

flits around just trying to get her head together. I'm 100 percent for skinnydipping, swinging or whatever else has been invented to keep us all from slipping into the Valley of the Dolls forever, but my husband is a 40-year-old *boy* who's still into cycling, sky-diving and things like that that leave me out.

Please try to find time to write back to one who is

Trapped in amber

Violet Simms

(my maiden name, because I no longer consider myself married to that clunk)

Williamsport, Pa.

Dear: Miss Xaviera Hollander,

Hi, I have just finished reading "The Happy Hooker" which awoke me to the fact that people live many different types of lives. Your own life has really amazed me and to say the least I found I couldn't put the book down.

I think you must be a very remarkable person to have revealed all these things you've done. You really do enjoy your life and cause a lot of others to enjoy theirs too.

I hope you didn't mind this short note but your book took me away from Vietnam into a dream type world most men try to visualize. You are also very beautiful.

Thank you again Miss Hollander for letting a stranger into your personal life.

Sincerely,

Danny Pfluger

Long Binh, Vietnam

Dear Mademoiselle Xaviera,

I recently read "The Happy Hooker" and I just had to write and tell you how much I enjoyed it! Not only did I find it fascinating as a story, but it also has a special interest for me. For the past five years I have been living a life very much like yours—not that I have as many opportunities in California or have your obvious administrative talents for making it pay.

I am 22, intelligent, good-looking and a "swinger." I also like money and would like to get into the business end. All I need is the practical know-how. I did get a lot of hints from your lay-it-on-the-line book, but I am really hoping you can find the time to give me more specific advice in how to get started in the "pleasure" industry. I've done a little free-lancing on my own, but the monetary rewards seem small compared to the eventual figure I had in mind, and I don't seem to be able to contact the "right" people. You know, those who are willing to pay for certain specialties.

I realize you must have gotten lots of letters since your book appeared, but I think you're shrewd enough to tell the difference between a genuine letter and a crank trick of some kind. I hope enough of my personality comes through to make this letter stick out from the crowd.

I really wish there was a way I could talk frankly to you and tell you a little more about myself. Aside from practical considerations, I'd really like to get to know you much better, even if only through a letter. In your book, you sound like such an interesting and fun person! That's not just a self-promoting compliment—it's really the way your personality came through to me in your book.

> Hoping to hear from you soon,
>
> Yvette Robinson
>
> San Jose, Calif.

Dear Miss Hollander,

Please forgive me for intruding on your busy life, but, I have been trying very hard to locate you for the past month and this is the first opportunity I've had to contact you personally.

Let me explain that I learned about you after reading your autobiography, which I enjoyed tremendously, but by the same token confused me a little. I don't know how to put it into words, what I want to make you believe, but after reading your book I realize you are the only one I know now that I can talk to and trust. I realize I am nobody special and am being very bold, as to ask you to help me, but there is no one else I can turn to. I hope, though, that upon receiving this letter you will write me. I would be in debt to you for the rest of my life.

Please don't take my letter lightly because right now the most important thing to me is to talk with you about something I can talk to no one else about.

Thank you for taking the time to read this and hoping to hear from you soon.

Respectfully and sincerely,

Emily Jane Grandgent

Charleston, W. Va.

Dear Miss Hollander:

Please help me. Like, HELP!

I have a wonderful relationship with a young lady and I think we are serious about each other. We really make it well together.

Except for one problem. She was rather inexperienced when I met her, but I never anticipated what seems like a bad sexual joke actually happening. To wit: is it normal for a woman to have 15 or 20 orgasms during one hour of sex! I never know when I've satisfied her as she's always ready for more of the same.

At first I thought this was fun. Real fantasy living. But reality has crept in and unless we work this out, I'm going to be a sexual casualty of the New Freedom. I mean, in a given 24 hours' time, I may be good for a triple header, with some extras thrown in, but if we keep this up, I'm going to be spending the *next* week in traction.

I mean, really, like HELP! Tell me what to do: should I hang in there, hoping this is just a phase of sexual precocity—I really care for her—or recognize my human limitations and find another, more "normal" female?

Should I ask her to see a doctor? I just don't know. She seems to be having a perfectly fine time, while I'm hanging loose—in the worse sense of that term.

Please do write,

Jerry Grose
University of Minnesota
Minneapolis, Minn.

Dear Miss Hollander,

We would like to discuss with you a personal matter involving our client who has contracted an unusual decease related to activities which you arranged for our client.

Yours,

Donald Runne
Sue, Grabitt & Runne
Attorneys at Law
New York, N.Y.

101

Dear Madam X,

Your book has turned out to be a sensation in America and no wonder. All in all, we're a very sexually naive people. I'll give you an example of what I mean.

In World War II, I served with the army in North Africa. I was only 19 at the time and one night some of my buddies took me to a live show they had already been to but didn't want to tell me about in advance. All I knew was that there was going to be some kind of gambling.

When we got there we got pretty good seats and I could see there was a kind of stage with five pallets on it. Most of the audience was Arab, with a sprinkling of GIs and Frenchmen. The five pallets were numbered and bettakers walked up and down the aisles taking bets on the different numbers.

After about ten minutes, the girls came out. They were all absolutely nude and, depending on your taste, they were one sexier than the next. There was a charming and petite Chinese girl, a lovely Arab with enormous breasts, a big-boned, blonde Caucasian who might have been Swiss or German or Scandinavian, the most beautiful Sudanese girl I ever saw in my life and a fifth girl who was exotically Eurasian. The girls all lay down on their pallets and waited.

Then a tall, muscular, mulatto-colored Berber with his head shaved appeared. The crowd nearly went wild with applause. He was totally naked too and you couldn't help but notice that even soft and limp he had the biggest cock I've ever seen in my life. It hung half way down his leg.

At a signal from the judge, he mounted the girl on pallet No. 1, the Sudanese. Her legs went up like flagpoles and he began to screw her slowly and steadily. After exactly one minute, a sort of bell rang, he got off, and now hard, moved over onto the girl on pallet No. 2, the white girl. She looked like she was having a ball, wrapped her long legs around him and refused to stop when the minute was up. The audience yelled "Foul!" and the judge had to pry her legs apart to uncouple them. Then, in turn, he fucked the Chinese girl, the Eurasian and the Arab girl.

When he had made the rounds, he began all over again with the girl on pallet No. 1.

By now I had learned how the betting worked. Whichever of the girls succeeded in making him come—and he seemed to have excellent control in holding off—the house paid off on that pallet number.

Well, as he continued to dip that enormous wang in them, the girls got hornier and hornier, and began to use every trick they knew. They clipped, they bit his ears, they moaned, they whispered what were probably obscenities into his ear. The audience loved it, the bettors all crying out encouragement to their "girls" to bring him to climax any way they could. The fourth time around, the white girl, trembling like a leaf, began to shriek with pleasure and came at least twice in the one minute he was in her. This must have turned him on, because as soon as he slid it into the moist opening of the Chinese girl he rammed it into her up to the hilt, made an animal like sound, and shot for almost the full minute. The crowd went wild with joy.

Well, after that we all went out and got laid.

Now I ask you, Xaviera, can you imagine a live show like that in Des Moines?

Yours for fancy fucking,

Lester Hadley, Jr.

San Francisco, Calif.

Dear Miss Hollander:
I have just finished reading your book and I would like to express my delightful enjoyment in reading it. You are truly a good writer and with great style. I hope your life is well and that eventually you will come back to America

103

when all the bullshit about your "voluntary" leaving has finally blown over.

Sincerely,

Arthur Ansonia
Harrisburg, Pa.

Dear Miss Hollander,

By the time this reaches you, I'm sure that you will have been inundated with mail about your book and your appearance on the Howard Smith show. As everyone has told you, you come across as a very warm, charming, vibrant (despite those "psychological scars"), sensitive, humorous female. I still have my doubts that you are representative of most of those who ply your former trade, but you certainly have shattered my myopic perspective on the nature of the "oldest profession." The irony which occurred to me is the fact that so-called straight relationships develop greater insensitivity, selfishness and hurt than your professional dealings have met. While I realize that the opportunity for a face-to-face meeting is quite remote, I nevertheless hope that one day we might become acquainted.

And now, here comes the zinger. Please believe my sincerity in all that I have said. I would greatly appreciate your steering me to someone equally capable and satisfying as you have obviously been for so many others. Please write as soon as it is possible. My body is beginning to atrophy. Seriously, in any case, thank you for your time and indulgence and hope to hear from you soon.

Respectfully yours,

Maurice Bernheimer
Branchville, N.J.

(The following letter was sent to Xaviera's publisher.)

Gentlemen:
Please send any clippings or press releases regarding Xaviera Hollander's book, "The Happy Hooker."
My literary club members and I have purchased several copies of the book and we are preparing a book discussion and review session.
Thank you for your help in advance.

Yours very truly,

Marlene Babich

Manchester, New Hamp.

Dear Miss Hollander:
I am enclosing a copy of the letter I have just written to the President. I have never before written to a President on any matter.
I have also *never* (a strong word) enjoyed a book as much as I did the one you've produced. If indeed you have to leave the country, may I wish you the best of luck in all your future undertakings.

With deepest respect,

Judson T. Blasingame

Clifton, N.J.

The President of the United States
Mr. Richard Nixon
The White House
1600 Pennsylvania Ave.
Washington D.C.

Dear Mr. President:
I was appalled to hear the outcome of the recent deportation hearings for Miss Xaviera Hollander.

While I have never gone to a prostitute myself, I am in favor of legalizing prostitution since I feel they perform a very necessary function.

If we can allow known communists to teach in our public schools, there is no reason we cannot allow an ex-prostitute to live in this great country of ours. Miss Hollander has paid her penalty and since she is no longer engaged in prostitution, I deplore the fact that she should be thrown out of the Country.

We would be much better advised to direct our energies at blocking un-American activities in our public institutions than to harass a woman whose only crime is honesty.

Your attention in this matter would be greatly appreciated.

Very truly yours,

Judson T. Blasingame
Clifton, N.J.

Dear Miss Hollander,
It is totally out of character for me to be writing this letter and it seems crazy that I am doing so. But perhaps you will understand, as your book indicates you've been into quite a few new, kinky things yourself in the past months.

I am writing to you out of a simple need to tell you how important your book was to me, and also how cogent I thought your comments were in this week's *Village Voice*.

Your book meant a great deal to me. For years I have been into one of the milder forms of the S&M scene you described so knowingly. Although you expressed the limits of your tolerance of some of the farther-out scenes—with which I definitely share your feelings—you dealt with the theme as just another of the multitude of varieties of that wonderful thing called sex. It meant a lot to me to hear this from a beautiful, intelligent woman such as yourself.

One of the problems of someone who is into one of the way-out areas of sexual preference is the great sense of isolation one feels. It is difficult enough in life just to find decent companionship from the opposite sex, but to find a woman whose temperament and general personal preferences in sex fit in with those of a mild masochist is extraordinary. But to hear you talk about your own attitudes on the subject gives me hope. Frankly I have never found this satisfactory, as it would seem there are very few girls who really understand this scene and are interested in it.

I hope some of your previous experiences with men who share my interests will help to convince you I'm not some kind of nut writing you this way. I'm a perfectly "normal" 42-year-old man who's been in public relations for the past 13 years.

Whatever your decision, I would appreciate your doing one thing. As you see I've enclosed a self-addressed stamped envelope. I would love it if you'd write to me, but if nothing else could you just seal it and send me the empty envelope so I'll know you at least received the letter? Your book meant something very special to me and, I'm sure, to many others, for which I can only say many thanks.

Sincerely yours,

Jerry Wilhelm
Haverstraw, N.Y.

AN ADVENTURE: NANCY AT THE DOOR

While still living in Toronto in September 1972, I was trying to concentrate on finishing some TV work. I had just moved into a luxurious hotel suite provided for me by the "Call Callei Show." The Indian girl who had stayed there before me had left it in an unbelievable mess. However, the special suite management had promised to send a maid to clean and tidy it up. But since the maid hadn't arrived yet, and I was just standing around with my luggage, I thought it would be better to start putting my things away and straighten up the suite myself.

Suddenly there was a knock at the door. I asked who it was and the answer was "Nancy." Thinking it was either the secretary from the show (whose offices were right next door) or the maid I was expecting, I opened the door. But it was neither. Instead, I found myself confronted by an attractive, very well-groomed brunette in her mid-thirties. Before I could even say hello, she threw her arms around me, hugged me passionately and kissed me on the mouth as ardently as if we were lovers. I responded; I responded more than I care to admit. But realizing that this unexpected encounter was going too far—and in the hall, no less—I finally pushed her away.

"Who are you?" I asked, bewildered.

"My name is Nancy," she said, her smoldering black eyes never leaving my face. "Please, Xaviera, let me come in and I'll explain."

Foolishly perhaps, I let her come in, while I picked up the expensive coat she had carelessly dropped on the floor. Since it gave me a few moments to collect my wits, I hung it in the closet. When I came back into the living room, Nancy was just about ready to fall apart;

she was sitting on the couch, trembling and on the verge of tears. I think she probably would have had a good bawling session right then and there if I had not immediately started to laugh. Her lipstick, smeared from her lips up to her elegant nose when I had pushed her head away, made her look like a circus clown. I got a hand mirror from my bedroom and made her look, and we both had a good laugh over it. Then she suddenly turned serious.

"Xaviera, don't you remember me? Take a good look at me. . . . I guess I look different fully clothed."

Guessing what I was thinking, she hurried on to say, "No, no, don't misunderstand me. We never had any scenes together or anything like that."

Pretty nervous now, she lit a cigarette and continued speaking at a very rapid rate before I had a chance to say anything. "I met you and your boy friend at the Conquistador Hotel in Puerto Rico on Washington's birthday. I was with my husband Bob, and we sat next to each other at the pool for almost a week. The men spent a lot of time discussing business. As a matter of fact, I even have one of your books that you personally autographed for me. . . . You remember what a hard time we had finding one of your books on the island?"

I **did** have a vague recollection of having met such a couple, but I couldn't honestly say I remembered her. So I just nodded.

"When we first met," she continued, "something started going on inside my head. And then when I read "The Happy Hooker," I got more and more turned on to you every day. But I hid my feelings and didn't dare discuss them even with you, since I thought that once you'd left I would forget all about you. You know, 'Out of sight, out of mind.'

"But I didn't. I simply couldn't. I kept fantasizing day and night about meeting you again and what it would be like to make love to you. I really got scared of my own feelings. Was I turning into some kind of a lesbian?"

Anxious that she would break down after all, I asked

112

her if she wanted a drink, but she just shrugged the idea away impatiently.

"At night I lay awake, restless, and my poor husband never quite realized that when he was holding me in his arms and kissing me it really was **you** I was making love to, **you** who caressed me. My fantasies took over more and more every day but particularly at night. Sometimes I caught myself hugging a pillow and pretending it was you. . . . Finally, guilt made me desperate enough to want to change. I was determined to rid myself of the desire to be with you and the foolish fantasy life I had created. I simply told myself that at 34 I was too old to be entertaining thoughts of new and exciting sexual adventures.

"The thing is I almost succeeded. What went wrong was that your pictures and newspaper articles about what you were doing kept popping up. And though I tried to deny it, when I saw photographs of you staring out at me, that same warm feeling I thought I had suppressed overwhelmed me all over again. I knew then that I simply had to find you, had to talk it over with you in all honesty and get it out of my system.

"But how could I do this? You had already left the country, and nobody could reach you. I wrote you a letter using the name and address of a girl friend—Sarah Klein. Naturally, I had to take her into my confidence and tell her about my obsession with you. It was just a short note, asking for your address and phone number, so that I could write you a longer letter or possibly call you regarding a problem I felt you might be able to help me with."

"I get so many letters," I said, "and I try to answer them all personally. But a lot of them are from sickies and weirdos. . . ."

"Xaviera, I feel like such a dumb bunny coming this way, unannounced. But you didn't answer my letter, and I was afraid if I called you, you wouldn't invite me to come. I got your address by calling your boy friend Larry in New York, and telling him I was an old friend of yours on my way to Canada, and could I have your address? I got his telephone number from my husband's address book while he was asleep; I remembered that he had taken it down for business reasons.

"Larry was kind enough to give me your address. I told my husband I was going to Canada for a few days to check out some design work. You may not remember, but I have a pretty responsible job as a buyer for one of the big Fifth Avenue department stores.

"So I took along the usual small bag I travel with. I caught a plane for Toronto, checked my bag at the airport and here I am.

"Please, Xaviera, don't turn me away. Let me stay here with you for a little while. Let me get to know you better, let me love you and let's do all the things I've dreamed about. Make me come till I scream for you to stop. I am so excited, I'm actually dying for you to make love to me.

"You're a fair person, Xaviera. You have a reputation for never hurting anybody. Please help me now with my problem."

By this time, after this touching emotional display, I was actually getting pretty horny, turned on by the sincerity of this girl-woman. At a loss for words, however, I suggested she slow down, stop talking and just relax for a few minutes. When she had done as I said, I took her by the hand and we walked through the bedroom into the bathroom. Picking up a housecoat on the way, I suggested that she freshen up by taking a nice bubble bath, and then make herself comfortable by putting on my morning gown. Her face was still smeared with lipstick, and I'm sure she was sweaty and uncomfortable from the trip. I excused myself and went back into the living room because I had a great many telephone calls to catch up on.

I must have been on the phone for 15 or twenty minutes, maybe longer, when I suddenly remembered Nancy. I jumped up and dashed into the bathroom, but she was not there. Then as I entered the bedroom, I got my second big shock of the day. I guess I should have been prepared for the scene that greeted my eyes, but truthfully I wasn't. Nancy was stretched out on the bed, her beautiful naked body all squeaky clean, smiling up invitingly at me.

I didn't need a second invitation. I quickly returned to the bathroom, took a bath and spent a few moments more applying deodorants. Throwing a hand towel over my shoulder, I nonchalantly walked into the bedroom As I joined Nancy on the bed, her eagerly awaiting arms enfolded me. Instead of letting me touch her, however, she guided my face to her large breasts, whispering: "Please, Xaviera, just lie still for a few minutes and let me fully savor that your wonderful naked body is in my arms at last. Please don't move, darling . . . I never dreamed that my wish would finally come true. . . ."

I lay in her arms, feeling the warmth of her body and the rigidity of her distended nipples. I was getting so horny that in another few minutes I think I would have come through sheer mental stimulation. After a few minutes of relaxing and sighing together, I felt her arm rubbing my back. I started to lick her, first her earlobes, then her neck down to her stiffened nipples, then all around her belly button, finally plunging into her delicious pussy as she gasped in pleasure.

All of this seemed to take an eternity. Her bush was heart-shaped, with the hairs cut fairly short. Holding each leg down with one arm, I started to flick at her clitoris with my tongue. (They don't call me the fastest tongue in town for nothing.) She was soon ready to explode. Her arms banged against the headboard frantically, her head rolled from side to side and low moans came out of her throat, building up to louder panting sounds.

I stopped and moved my head away for a moment, hoping to drive her just a little crazy. I could see that I was indeed succeeding, as she grabbed my hair and tried to pull my head back down on her bush. I wanted her to beg me to start eating her again. I turned my body around so that my legs were near her head. I bent forward and wrapped my arms around her voluptuous hips and ass. Her thighs seemed divine as I spread them apart and once again began to eat around the small triangle until I hit the rose. I inserted my index finger deep into her moist cunt, then replaced the finger with my eager tongue.

This time I moved my tongue very gently, in order not to hurt her. Once again I heard the sounds gurgling in Nancy's throat. She was so wet that I could really taste the juices from her slobbering cunt. I was so lost in what I was doing that I didn't realize that Nancy, in her own way, was trying to lick my clitoris and playing with me with her fingers. She manipulated and vibrated my clitoris every imaginable way, then ended up squeezing it until it was almost painful.

In the next ten minutes, Nancy must have had at least three orgasms, while I felt myself approaching a point where I thought I might go out of my mind with lust. I turned around, facing her, and kissing her deeply on the lips, placed my leg between her thighs. Then I began a pumping motion, as a man would while fucking a woman, rubbing my cunt against hers. Soon I felt the first stirrings of what I knew was going to be a fantastic orgasm. I started to scream, and at the same time I could feel Nancy wildly pumping and having another orgasm. When we both had come, we lay entwined in each other's arms in a near faint.

We must have fallen asleep in this position, because almost an hour later I felt Nancy stirring in my arms, trying to get up without awakening me. Opening my eyes a moment later, I saw the light on in the bathroom. In my dazed state, I heard the shower running. About five minutes later, thinking I was still asleep, she crept back into bed and snuggled into my arms once more.

In a short while, we started making love again, and many hours and several orgasms later, I finally urged Nancy to get up. Larry and my editor were coming from New York and I didn't particularly feel like having them walk in on a scene like this. I explained all this to Nancy and asked her to please get dressed. I called the desk and arranged for a room for her for the night. I told her that we would get together some time tomorrow, but that I didn't know what my schedule would be since this was the first time I would be working with my editor. I explained that I would improvise some sort of schedule, and then call her and make arrangements to see her again.

Reluctantly, Nancy got dressed and after a parting hug and kiss, she disappeared into the elevator. She had to go back to the airport to get her bag, then return to the hotel.

The following day I became so involved with the preparations for working on my manuscript that I completely forgot about Nancy. When I finally remembered, it was with a twinge of guilt. However, since she hadn't called me I decided not to call her, figuring that she was probably dead tired after the exhausting sex of the day before. Also, I had no idea when I would be able to sneak away to meet her.

About 3 o'clock in the afternoon I started to become apprehensive, since I still had not heard from her. I called her room but no one answered. When I called the desk to leave a message for her, I was told that she had checked out, but that she had left a letter for me.

I rushed downstairs and was given a sealed white envelope with my name on it. Sitting down on a couch in the corner of the lobby, I hurriedly tore the envelope open. Inside there was a sheet of large white stationery. It read:

My dear, dear Xaviera,

I don't know if our paths will ever cross again. If they don't, I want you to know that you are one of the most wonderful people I have ever met. After last night I realize that everything I built up in my head about you came out of a great need to make love to you. I hope you understand that once I made love to you and you made love to me, that it satis-

117

fied all of the fantasies that I had been living with these past months.

I am going back to my husband now, and I am sure that I will never have this type of longing again. You gave me everything that I ever could want or expect from a woman. I loved every second of it, but it also purged me of all the anxieties of this type of love. I guess I simply wasn't meant to be a lesbian.

I guess I'll end up being a one-man woman again. I want you to know that you are everything I expected and more, and once again thank you. Please don't be upset that I chose to leave in this manner, but I thought it would be better for both of us.

Once again, God bless you, Xaviera, for letting me open my heart to you and for the most thrilling sexual moments of my life.

All my love,
Nancy

I folded and put away the letter, not knowing exactly how I felt about it but thinking that maybe we were both better off for having had the experience. What it had lacked in length of time it certainly had made up for in intensity. Anyway, I had a lot of work ahead of me now, and it was probably just as well that I didn't have to worry about keeping a new girl friend happy. Though I **did** feel a little blue when I thought that I would probably never again see the heavenly body of the multi-orgasmic Nancy, the horny girl-woman who had come to me so boldly.

* * *

Jophiera

I listened to you on the radio last night. I don't know if Xaviera is your real name or not but you sound very much like a Dutch girl that destroyed me. It's a long story. Her name was Yvette van der Lind. She lived in Hilversum. Nobody knows about her any more at her home or the school she used to attend in Utrecht.

If you are Yvette come back. I always loved you and I treated you like that just to test your feelings. But you failed the test. You never came back and you fucked everybody up. I still remember and this is the torture. If you are not her you sound very much like her, although she was not as intelligent as you.

So Jophiera (I hate this name) you are a very interesting person. I want to mee you and hear some Dutch cursings.

I don't propose to be a client. I know you are out of the business now and I never payed for it anyway. I never do, and I never accepted money for it.

So that's the story. I have a small tent and a convertible VW. Maybe we can go camping (I'm a nature lover) or I don't know maybe just to see you and say "Hi." To see if you have blue eyes and short blonde hair like Yvette.

I'm a student from Greece (I'll teach you some belly dancing it's beatifull). I'm finishing school next year and will gon on to Germany for something higher. I'll work then in the ships for a few years to see a little bit around and then I'll get married to anybody just to have kids. I don't know if I can love. Now I'm working as an engineer in Troy to make some money. I have a small beard (which doesn't prevent me for some linguistics if I'm in the moods and there is togetherness).

That's it. The rest you'll see. I'm not gonna make a fool of myself describing although this is irrelevant. I'm not proposing myself as a lover but as a friend who hates Holland, and its fucked up people. If you decide not to answer it's all right. Maybe just send a photo.

Vassili Dmitroff
Troy, N.Y.

Dear Xaviera:

I have just read your entertaining, informative, delightful and very horny book, and I would like to know (quite seriously) if you could teach ME the art of love-making. I'm sure that you have probably gotten quite a few letters like this, but I am quite serious. I am quite willing to pay you for it. I have made love to a few women, and my sexual and love-making expertise is not what it should be. I would appreciate a reply if you could find the time. Thank you.

EXCITEDLY,

Mike Dahlberg
Waco, Texas

Dear Xaviera Hollander,

I have read "The Happy Hooker" and I want you to know I consider it a classic. Your photograph alone makes me wish I could have known you. Like Helen of Troy, if you had wanted to, your face could have launched a thousand ships.

I believe in the right of adults to mutually enjoy each other in any way they see fit. That's why I hope to see the day when prostitution is legal in every state in the union. If it is and you have such a house of pleasure, we are going to know each other. I may be a little older than your typical customer, but I am still very young physically.

Although I have a lot of friends, I don't have the kind you have been to others. The world needs more straightforward and understanding people like you, people who derive pleasure from giving pleasure and vice versa. Anyone who denies this is nothing but a hypocrite.

My respect for you is very great and I wish I could have been numbered among your friends. You dared to live your life in an uninhibited and completely honest manner. Not many people can make that claim, though many like

120

to pretend they're "liberated." But while they were living their "uptight" lives, you brought a lot of pleasure into the lives of others. I wish I could have been part of it.

All the happiness and good fortune in the world to you!

Sincerely,

Clarence Drosset

Scottsdale, Ariz.

Dear Miss Hollander:

I'm reading your book with great pleasure, but I sure wish I could finish it.

You see, I'm afraid to take the book home, where my wife will see it, so I try to read it on the job, and—well, I'm an elevator operator.

So I read a snatch here, and a snatch there—hey, NO pun intended—and at this rate it's going to take me six weeks to finish your book.

At least it makes the job less boring.

Your (slow) reader,

Peter W. Amenta

Chicago, Ill.

Dear Miss Hollander:

I have just finished reading "The Happy Hooker" and found it quite a book, a bit perverted but then that's life.

I would like a personal appointment with you in regards to writing a similar book for me. I think I can match "The Happy Hooker," not with personal experiences but with what I have observed and known about human affairs intimately—with details. I am a woman of 50 and have been an innkeeper or a barmaid for most of my life and I could tell some stories no one would believe, not even if they had seen it with their own eyes. The things the people do—"how they get their kicks"—when you think you've seen them all, someone comes up with something new. It never ceases to amaze me.

Anyway, I would like your advice on putting together a paperback book. Maybe you could advise me on what direction to take, whether I should write it as a "story" or in simple book form. If you are interested in helping me write it, my book could make "Peyton Place" look like a Methodist ice cream social.

Hoping to hear from you soon.

I remain,

Prudence Joyce Jones
Lakewood, N.J.

Dear Miss Hollander,

You doubtless receive many letters about your book. I imagine this one is not much different from the others. It has to be written, however.

To begin with, you have already provided many intriguing hours for me. I have read your book twice, and am considering reading it a third time—it's that good.

I have always thought prostitution should be legalized. We are all prostitutes in a manner of speaking, I as well as you, although I make my living as a skilled carpenter. Nonetheless, people pay for my time as they do yours.

Because I enjoy eating pussy, I have sometimes wondered if I were normal, yet the more I read it seems everybody is doing it. After reading your book, I no longer feel "kinky," and am further convinced that this, like any other aspect of love, is an expression of deep feeling. For a sensitive man to be able to drive a woman sexually out of

122

her mind, when probably all else may have either failed or fallen short, is the most wonderful feeling in the world.

The world needs women like you, as long as there are men in it. How foolish society is not to recognize yours as a skill, no less important than that of the attorneys, doctors, writers with whom you associate. How many bad marriages could have been avoided if someone like you were there as a consultant!

If you feel it would help, you may use this letter as one man's testimonial in your behalf in any courtroom. It is not the ramblings of a freak or wierdo but of a normal red-blooded American.

I wish I knew you—since reading your book, I know what a void it is not to have known one of the most dynamic and exciting women of our time. Should I ever get to New York again, well that may be another chapter.

Good luck for now.

Sincerely,

Robert Ames
Decatur, Illinois

Miss Xaviera Hollander,

I have just finished "The Happy Hooker" and wanted to do a little more than reading. I chose writing you a letter. I hope you do receive this—the last time I did this was in the 5th grade when I wrote to Johny Unitas—never received a reply.

It is a rare occasion when I meet someone who shares so many of my views. It is like reading good fiction, with the difference being that the main character is actually "real." Your opinions on sex, love, ships in the night, race and truth parallel mine with uncanny closeness.

But the trait I like the best is your unselfishness—a concern about others. To you everyone is an individual who needs a little praise, attention, respect, with all the honesty and cheerfulness that it can be given. How tremendous that this main character doesn't live only in the pages of your book!

Seriously, though, I really admire you, hope you never change, and also hope that our paths will cross someday.

Best wishes forever,

Melvin Leiman

Wells Fargo, N. Dak.

Dear Ms. Hollander,

Loved your book! Boy, what a head trip it was. Please continue the good life.

That's it, I guess. Hate being long-winded.

So long,

Fred R. Margo,

Dayton, Ohio

Dear Miss Hollander:

Dug your book a whole lot and wonder if you could answer a question for me. Or maybe at least consider what could be a problem for some guys.

You see, I'm into older women—I mean, I really truly dig older women—but whenever I make an overture to some great looking woman, I clam up and don't get out even my first well-rehearsed lines. I stand there like some dumb schmuck—or deaf mute, even—and she smiles at me and I sort of mutter and talk to myself.

Do you have any idea of what kind of opening line would make sense for me to use? I mean, I need something that will really turn on an older woman. I'm 22,

124

which isn't being a kid by any means, and I feel like such a dope when I get my sights on an older woman and before you know it my nuts are boiling over, and I can't think of anything to say!

Please, how do I handle this kind of situation? How would you like me to talk to you, for instance?

Anything you can tell me will be deeply appreciated.

H. Ward Kaminski
Van Nuys, Calif.

Dear Xaviera:

After reading your book I wanted to write and lay it on you.

I think you are one of—or the most completely honest —woman I have heard about or know about.

In addition you are an unusually attractive woman. I would enjoy and appreciate meeting and simply sitting and rapping with you.

Xaviera, it seems some minds are rather similar. I like the way you think. I dig women the way men turn you on —that is the reason my ex-wife divorced me and split with my two sons.

I was caught with some swinging women too many times, however I like it this way. I am or feel free and clean—with no hang-ups.

Unfortunately there are not enough lovely women such as yourself around. I am sure you know some people are going to come down on you because of your book—well, sugar, do not—and I am sure you will not—let it bother you. You tell it like it is, and in my mind that is what's important.

Most certainly I hope to meet you someday. You are my kind of people—a free spirit who does and says what she thinks or what turns you on.

Enclosed is a little picture. You do with it as you like— throw it away, give it away, I hope you will keep it. My

125

boat is just behind me, a small one but it moves me. I do a great deal of water skiing.

Xaviera, I would very much appreciate a card or note from you.

I picked up on this rather unusual stationery because it reminded me of the many times I would be alone at the beach—I lived at both Laguna and Newport beach—and I would watch the sun go down behind the sea.

Baby, you be what you are and do your thing. To hell with what those fucked up (mentally mostly) people may think.

I hope this reaches you.

My Regard (for being you)

Gene Faraday
Coral Gables, Fla.

Dear Xaviera,

I've been bisexual since I was 16. I am 28 now, considered quite attractive and have a very busy sex life. Even with all the sex I get, though, I still like to jack off and I don't mean just one-two-three, here we go "whee."

For me masturbation is a slow, delicate, almost Japanese art. As much as I love sex with a good partner, I still can't give up my solo flights. Am I more sexually charged up than most, or should I start taking cold showers?

Sincerely,

Cedric R. Slayton II
Rapid City, N. Dak.

Dear Miss Hollander:

Even though I have not yet finished "The Happy Hooker," I am struck with an intriguing idea which prompts this letter.

I am fascinated by your philosophy; I thought it would be most interesting to meet with you with the idea of gathering more biographical information which might then be published in the form of an article (we could call it "The Happy Hooker Revisited," or something like that.)

I am a psychiatric social worker and a writer, and I have been published before. If you were to share my enthusiasm about this idea, it might be enlightening to take an in-depth look at your life as a context for your views. Although you touch upon your background in the book, there is obviously much more that could be explored.

Of course, I would be dishonest not to admit that my professional experience makes me want to understand more about you, since you seem to be such an unusual person.

If you would be interested in meeting with me to discuss the possibility of an article, please let me know. I would be able to come to New York to see you.

Sincerely,

Mildred B. Richardson, Ph.D.

University of Maryland

Dear Miss Hollander,

I loved your book and have only one question to ask. Are you single? If you are, would you be interested in getting married? The reason I'm asking is I'd love to get married to someone like you and have a large family, say six boys and three girls.

After reading your fascinating book I've decided you're just about the sweetest girl in the world and would make any man a wonderful wife. Please write and tell me your answer and please pretty please write to me and be my friend.

If you do not decide to make me "the happiest man in the world," I shall have to propose to someone else.

Thank you for a wonderful experience just reading your knock-out book!

All my love,

Duard Atwood

Marshalltown, Iowa

P.S. I think you're marvelous!

Dear Miss Hollander,

I just finished reading "The Happy Hooker" and felt very empathetically toward you and your profession.

I wonder if you could do me a tremendous favor? I am going with a wonderful boy and want to give him something special for his birthday (March 11th). Could you possibly autograph a copy of your book for him as it would make a spectacular present? I've enclosed $10, as I feel you should have the money for postage and taking the trouble.

Anyhow, could you write on the fly leaf: "To Seymour Schwartz, Happy Reading" (or something like that) and sign your name?

I will be ever so grateful if you help me make my boy friend's birthday a most memorable occasion.

Wishing you all the best,

Ellie Barton

Washington, D.C.

P.S. If you forward the book to me, I'll have it fancy gift wrapped for the occasion.

Dear Miss Hollander:

I recently finished reading your book and found it very enjoyable. It is of such great interest and such good reading because it discusses so informatively and intimately a subject that is so near and needed by most of us.

The reason for my writing to you is that I would like so much to meet you. I am 42 years old, married, have two daughters and am considered a fairly successful businessman. I do not feel that I have the basic rudiments for my sex life as I have for my professional background.

In your book you write so informatively and seem to imply that you take a great deal of personal interest in your clients. I am not a crank, rather just an average man who believes that association with expertise in any field, whether it be medicine, law, teaching or prostitution can lead to more expertise in any area one is interested in. If a "layman" can find someone who seems to have the charm and kindness that you have, he can consider himself most fortunate.

Consequently, if I may be so bold as to impose upon you, I would greatly appreciate your mailing me your card, so that I may call you and arrange an appointment with you.

Cordially,

James W. Nixon

East Orange, N.J.

Xaviera:

This is a little going-away thing to hang on your wall when you move back home.

It's called a God's Eye, originated by the Mexicans, who hung them in their homes as a symbol of good fortune and peace and to ward off forces of evil.

Even though you got into what you did because of a reaction to a hurt, I really dig what you had to say about

129

it—so I give you this, and I'm really sorry I keep missing you on the phone.

Even my mother got into your book. "This is disgusting," she said at first, but she kept on reading, gobbling up every page and enjoying it!

Actually, I don't like boys *or* girls—but men and women, and even though I've accepted the fact that I can turn on to women, I can't imagine it would be any good beyond an occasional diversion, because there's *one little thing missing:* a nice big penis!

We're looking forward to your next book—hurry!

My best wishes,

Carol E. Wolff

Little Rock, Ark.

Dear Miss Hollander,

Hi! I enjoyed reading "The Happy Hooker," but there are two things I'd like to take up with you. I especially enjoyed the part where you rated lovers according to national background, you know? Well, what you said about the Italians—I don't know, but when I was there I found them extremely handsome and extremely charming. But when it was time for "Lights out!" they demonstrated all the maturity and love-making know-how of a five-year-old bedwetter. Really, all they want is mammas, always wanting to suck on your breasts and all that. Of course I realize you've had much more experience with them, so maybe it was just my luck to meet the wrong ones. Including one faggot who didn't even know he was a faggot.

The only feature of the book that did upset me, Xaviera, and I gotta be honest, is how many times you used the word "little." Perhaps I'm just being oversensitive as I am rather petite (4'11''), but after a while it began to sound condescending. Maybe it's only a habit and you don't really mean anything by it, but I think you ought to watch for it more carefully in your next book (which I'm dying to read!).

Yours truly,

Gwen Suthwell
Detroit, Mich.

Dear Miss Hollander,
I understand from my son that he had some kind of sexual congress with you in Puerto Rico. I find this quite surprising as I felt we'd chaperoned him quite satisfactorily.

I was considering legal action against you for seducing a minor, but then I realized that you had probably done *my* work for me. Not that in this day and age a father has to do such things for his male sons, but the thought is appreciated, nonetheless.

Samuel R. Becker
Bay City, Michigan

Dear Miss H,
Read your fantastic book and admire your honesty and agree in the hope of eventual legalized prostitution. (No, I am not one myself.)

I am a 38-year-old housewife with three kids and though I have always had a very strong sexual appetite, have always been "good." But this hasn't interfered in my interest in men, those luscious creatures, and enjoy them far more than women—in every conceivable way.

My 13-year-old daughter read your book and really flipped for it (especially the part about Helga) and when the boy is ready (he's 11, but a little young for his age) I'm going to pass it on to him. What better way to learn the facts of life about the birds and bees, right?

If you should ever find yourself in the Bayou area, we would certainly like to have a drink together and compare notes with you.

Sincerely,

Mrs. Victoria L'Heureuse
Baton Rouge, La.

Dear Miss Xaviera,

If you or any of your girl friends are ever in the Bay area, I would be delighted if you would stay with me, at least as long as I am not married.

I live in a one bedroom apartment in Sausalito, but in several months I will be moving into a home in Cupertino.

As much as I love to be loved and give love, I never have enough, strange as it seems.

I hope you can take time out from your busy schedule to write me a note and maybe drop in on me.

Your books are marvelous.

Sincerely,

Bernie Gerson
Sausalito, Calif.

Dear Miss Hollander,

This is the second time I am writing to you and have had no response yet. I'm not surprised—I know you must have a full schedule. You can't imagine how much I am looking forward to a letter from you, though.

I know you must think me a very foolish person, a complete stranger who writes to you as openly as I did the first time. Usually I am considered very sensible, but there are some things you just can't put aside. It's not easy keeping your feelings bottled inside yourself. You have become like a second life to me because you have been able to do things I would never be able to.

I often lie awake at night and wonder what it's like. I suppose it's the attention I crave most and the feeling of being wanted and not handled roughly or without feeling!

Compared to yours, my life is dull and unadventurous. I have four children and spend most of my day cooking and cleaning. Don't misunderstand me—I love my family very much, but like most women I need a different kind of love also.

Do you mind if I write to you once in a while? I assure you I am not a hysterical crackpot who'll never give you a moment's peace. I just need the reassurance that someone in the world knows and understands my feelings.

God bless you, Xaviera, for helping so many women look honestly into their hearts.

Sincerely,

Mrs. Theodora Callaghan
York, Pa.

Dear Madame X,

Since you spent some time in the Tombs, I started out to read your book, since I was curious about it. But right on page 2 you insult us with your reference to "bull-dyke matrons" in the Tombs.

I've been working in the Tombs for 12 years as a matron and I've seen some awful scum come thru. But as to myself and most of my co-workers, we always try to treat them as if they were "ladies."

I don't deny that there may be some lesbians among the matrons who take advantage of some of the young girls. But most of the matrons are like me, with husbands at home who worry that some drug-crazed "bull-dyke prostitute" might not decide to stick a shiv into one of us just for kicks.

I think you owe us an apology, Miss High and Mighty.

Mrs. Mildred Martindale

Union City, N.J.

Dear Miss Hollander,

I have just completed your book—my husband, an engineer, and I, a former schoolteacher and mother of a three-year-old boy—are both in our early thirties. I have a feeling we are missing a lot. Neither of us are ready for swinging—and we are rank amateurs at pleasing each other at this point—

Ironic, isn't it—We read a great deal about child raising, keep abreast of the news, research purchases and take assorted courses—Yet neither of us has gotten past a rudimentary knowledge of satisfying each other physically—

Where could we go to help fill this gap? Are there any books you would recommend that instead of being clinical —really give the "how to" of satisfying one another? You mentioned your possibly lecturing—are you planning a tour that includes the Midwest in the near future?

I am looking forward to hearing from you and am hoping you are in the process of writing another book (if you'll excuse the bad pun) "Tricks of the Trade—Explained."

Thank you for sharing your interesting life with us and opening up our minds—

Wishing you every happiness,

Mrs. Laura Hayes

Des Plaines, Ill.

Dear Xaviera:

Remember me? I'm the Lebanese film major that talked to you in the Pickwick Book Store. You mistook me for a browser at first but I meant business. . . .

I was somewhat surprised at your writing Room 282 [deleted] in response to my question "What are you doing tonight?" Sometimes a little gamble pays off. I took you to my apartment in Ocean Beach and learned much from you, oh Woman of the world. Then you had to catch a plane to N.Y. in the morning. And now you're miles and worlds away.

It's nice to dream, isn't it?

I won't forget you soon.

Omar Vashili

[address deleted]

Dear Miss Hollander:

Ordinarily I wouldn't bother such a busy person like yourself, but I wondered if you'd come up against this kind of thing. I know this hasn't been part of your professional life, but maybe it happened to you in the midst of one of your several love affairs as depicted in your first book.

To clear away the mystery, it's because my husband has marvelous orgasms and then can't get an erection for maybe two-three hours, is why I'm writing. I'm perfectly happy with this present arrangement, but he feels we should be back at it again in twenty minutes. I certainly wouldn't object to this, but it isn't a prerequisite for my happy sex life.

My husband, though, has read all the new books and thinks he should be performing miracles.

Frankly, he never complained of this until the night when we were in bed with another couple and he noticed the other guy could come back in 10-15 minutes. But that guy didn't last as long as we did, so comparative statistics are really meaningless, aren't they??

Yours sincerely,

Frieda M. Walsh

Cork, Ireland

Dear Xaviera,

Please permit a member of the world's "second oldest profession" to say how much he enjoyed your book. I do think the chapters on "kinky" behavior in sex should have been shortened or left out altogether. They are the only parts I found dull. But the book itself is like a beacon of truth.

I think you have performed a double service to the American public in being so candid about the oldest profession—and in doing so, writing such a readable book. I haven't enjoyed a book so much since I read Thornton Wilder's "The Woman of Andros."

Cordial regards,

Dr. H. H. Parkinson

Chevy Chase, Md.

Dear Miss Hollander,

I'd like to take this opportunity to tell you how much I was impressed with your book, which I found the most informative piece of reading I've done on the subject.

I guess I found your book so fascinating because I am 33 and single and have never had sex relations with a member of the opposite sex. My parents are Lutherans, so between their strict teachings and my own self-denial so that I can share my erotic initiation with my wife-to-be (whoever she may be) are the only reasons I haven't looked for sex. But if appetite has anything to do with it, I can assure you that I am otherwise sexually normal.

Sex is never discussed in my family. So I do have areas of ignorance that perhaps someone my age shouldn't have. I do believe that if I were ever in New York and wanted to have the right kind of first sexual experience, I would probably seek out someone with your kind of unique and total experiences.

Let me conclude by saying you're one of the most attractive young women I have ever seen and I will feel myself very lucky if I get someone half as pretty as you. I wonder—could you send me a small inscribed photo of yourself? That would make me happier than I can say.

I admit that I must have a real crush on you, Xaviera, and I even keep a picture of you hidden in my room (it wouldn't do for my mother to find it).

Most sincerely yours,

Donald Baylor
Topeka, Kansas

Dear Xaviera Hollander,
Could you please recommend a Manhattan house of prostitution for a college student who has had but modest sexual experience? Expense would prove to be no difficulty.

Let me add that I find your attitude on sex very adult.

Thank you,

Rolfe Wainscott
Penn State University
University Park, Pa.

Dear Xaviera,

I can't tell you how much it saddens me that you are leaving the country, and this is just to let you know that you can always consider me among your friends and fans in America.

I met you last week while you were autographing "The Happy Hooker" in a bookstore near my office. I was wearing a long lavender cape over black velveteen hot pants and you said I was the sexiest-looking girl in the store! My head still hasn't come down from the clouds. I also treasure the clever and sweet note you wrote in my copy of your book. I read it over and over again!

Even after such a brief meeting, your charm and magnetism will stay with me for a very long time. There are not that many feelingful people like you in the world, Xaviera.

I know wherever you are you'll make a splash, but I do hope that eventually you do return to the U.S. When you do, you can always find a friend at the address below.

Affectionately,

Ellen Kline

Great Neck, L.I.

(Editors' Note: Among Ms. Hollander's most devoted correspondents was J. Anthony Boynton of Council Bluffs, Iowa. He wrote a number of letters, which grow in fervor with each succeeding letter. The following are three of the several he wrote. Mr. Boynton is a sad man, but, in his own way, quite a free spirit.)

Dear Miss Hollander:

Hi . . . How's one, if not the best looking woman in America, doing? After seeing you on the "Lou Gordon Show" all I can say is "WOW!" "Hot dam!" How can one female have so much? Yes, Miss Hollander, you're just the type of woman who gives me wet dreams at night.

Another thing I like about you is your attitude toward sex. You're not ashamed to admit that you have engaged in love making with another female and you have no hang ups about saying that you like sex.

I have a problem I am hoping you can help me solve. Five years ago I was wounded in Vietnam, leaving me partially paralized and confined to a wheelchair. So you see my problem and if there is any way, or any where we might be able to meet discreetly for an evening of love making, the reason I say discreetly is because I am living with my parents.

Looking at your photo on the book jacket, and I sincerely hope you take this as a complement, I get a knot in my groin and the urge to masturbate. After reading the book, I now know what and how a house with class and style should be operated. The only trouble, I have yet to hear of any such house in the Council Bluffs area.

My main problem at this time is not knowing if I'm impotent or not. However I do know I'm capable of getting an erection, but if I could keep it up long enough to have a good lay is something I don't know. It is for this reason that I have been directing my interest toward the French culture. Also, I know from times I have had women, most seem to enjoy and get a better orgasm from a man's tongue then from his cock. Tell me if you also find this to be true.

I figure if a woman as lovely as you can't get me aroused, then no women would be able to. I'm also sure with all the years that you've been in the business of selling your body, you must have come up with some not too far out tricks I could try.

If you could take a minute and sign a photo, any photo, of yourself and send it back to me, it would be greatly appreciated. So long and good luck in everything you set out to do, and thanks for listening to my problems.

Yours forever,

J. Anthony Boynton
Council Bluffs, Iowa

My Dearest Xaviera,

To say I was overjoyed to receive the pictures, with the exciting little notes written on them, would be an understatement. In fact, Xaviera, to be honest with you, I can't think of an adjective in the English language which could come anywhere near describing my feelings. The fact that you did reply shows that you have more of a heart and are capable of more understanding then the righteous people who condemn you, just because you love the natural feeling you get when you are being screwed and don't give a damn who knows.

The pictures you sent, Xaviera, were out of this world and they got me very aroused. So much so, that I wished I could climax and could once again enjoy masturbation.

True, anyone with eyes could see that you were built, but like a brick shit house! I never thought for a moment that you had such lovely breasts, two perfectly pear shaped just waiting to be aroused. I still can't understand why a woman with a bod and looks like yours isn't married by now.

The picture that really sent me right up the wall with desire was the one with you sucking on some guys finger, on which you wrote these wonderful words "if this finger were your cock, I'd know what to do with it" which I'm sure you would, if only we could get together, I'm sure it would be wonderful. With your tongue going around the head of my penis and gently sliding along the length of it and you ever so gently taking each nut in your mouth, first the right then the left.

Anyways, darling, while you were doing this, I would be exploring the depths of your womenhood, darting my tongue in and out arousing your by now very hard and excited clitoris, sending waves of pleasure throughout your body. Delighting in knowing that the love juices from your cunt were mixing with my juices, making a delicious cocktail of ectasy.

Darling, I've read your book six times all ready and if I read it any more I'll know it by heart word for word. But I am finally realizing that you are much more than two beautiful tits, a cunt and an ass. Your a whole and complete women and a very pretty one at that.

Then theres the picture of you standing there, with some guy behind you, with both his hands full of your sweet, lovely suckable tits. On which you signed "love, Xaviera."

Last but not least is the one which shows a full view of you and on which you suggested that I lay on my stomach and think of your body and drill a hole in my sheet. Then when I was aroused slide a pillow under me and rub my penis against it until I had an orgasm. Well anyways darling, I tried what you said, but didn't have any luck.

I'm sure its not the pictures you sent, for I can't see how you could possibly have pictures of yourself which are sexier. But maybe, and I would deeply appreciate it, if you could possibly send me some pictures showing you playing with yourself, pictures in which your exciting pussy is in full view. Maybe then I could have the orgasm I dream every night of having.

Could you send me the address of any houses of pleasure which you know of in the Council Bluffs area? I think I would be much better off with a women who knows just what she's doing. What do you think?

I had better be running as I want to get this into today's

mail. So-long and happy screwing and may your orgasms be many and strong.

With all my love,

J. Anthony Boynton
Council Bluffs, Iowa

My luscious Xaviera,

Hi, how is the most succulent woman in the world doing? I sincerely hope with all my heart, you don't mind me writing you so often. To be quite truthful, I think, no I know, I have a crush on you and am mad about your body and you. Xaviera, if given the chance, I would try to be anything you would want me to be. Anything from a mad fucker, to a crazy pussy and tit eater. Yes, anything. You could depend on me being your complete slave and your every wish would be my command.

However, I would not be a passive slave nor would I delight in taking a spoon, because I thought it would please you, and eating your shit. To me this would be degrading and I'm sure if we were to engage in these activities I think we would soon loose all respect for one another. Don't get me wrong, I do enjoy doing somethings that some might think kind of far out, like I think it would be really exciting laying in the bathtub with you standing over me with your legs spread and take turns pissing all over one another.

To me, a well-placed tongue can be much more exciting than any of the things some of the freaks that come to you, ask you to do. It sure would be super, to have my penis swell up while in you, making it impossible for us to part. On top of that, if life could be one long orgasm for the both of us, that would be happiness. I know for a fact if my desire to have sex with you could be harnessed, it would be enough power to light a city.

In my wild wonderful dreams I always see us together, naked, me running my tongue and hands gently along the inside of your long shapely leg, starting at your foot and ending at that fascinating, sensitive bridge of skin that connects your vagina with your anus.

Also darling, I sometimes see myself standing directly behind you, kissing the soft cheeks of your bottom and running my tongue along the length of your crack of your buttocks. With my organ erect and against your rump and one hand on each of your perfect tits and you bending over so as to better accommodate the entry of my penis into your anus and as I enter, ever so slowly and as my cock gets accustomed to the depths of your rectum, your hips begin to go into a spasmodic motion and as you begin to quiver and moan softly the moans of pleasure and delight, I ejaculate, filling your soft warm ass with my hot sticky semen.

Have to be running you beautiful cunt you. Be good, ha, ha, and don't do anything I wouldn't do. Think of me when you climax and have your orgasm.

Write, as I am hard and waiting.

With all my love,

J. Anthony Boynton
Council Bluffs, Iowa

Madam Hollander,
I've read your book, "The Happy Hooker." I am very satisfied with it, but most of all I want to wish you happiness in your profession. I personally think that "if a person enjoys making another happy, no one should try to stop them."

I have always enjoyed going with several boys at one time, or should I say in one night. I did until I got pregnant, but by the man I loved and married. Since my husband enjoys my teaching him new positions, I would like to learn more. I think that that you could teach me.

I am black, 20 years old. This may seem odd to you, but I would like to be taught by you the tricks of the trade. In other words, I'm *asking* and *begging* you teach me the way out positions you know about in sex. Since the age of 12, I have committed incest, adultery and cheated on all my boy friends. But now I can have sex with my husband and relax and laugh about the past.

But he has difficulty satisfying me. He has to use masturbation then normal sex or he has to force himself to continue after he climaxes in order to make me climax. And I'm a strong comer, who can come 10-12 times a night. Please help me.

Invite me to New York to really enjoy sex the way it should be. Three days is all I ask. Please. You enjoy making people happy, "Madam Xaviera Hollander, please make me happy sexually."

Mrs. Winona Jackson

Atlanta, Georgia

Dear Miss Hollander,

Can't tell you how much I enjoyed reading "The Happy Hooker." I think it's criminal what the government is doing to you and I especially deplore your forthcoming deportation. For what? Having written an honest book?

Xaviera, I wonder if you could let me know—directly or indirectly—about the stud services for men in the New York area. I don't get in very often, but when I do I would appreciate having a couple of addresses.

Hope life continues to smile on you, kid.

Sincerely,

B.J. Padgett

Dallas, Texas

Dear Xaviera,

This letter is to let you know I just finished your book and enjoyed every paragraph and page.

It's damn exciting to know there are really women like you who, for their own good reasons, best express themselves and their own deepest feelings by making love.

I am no different than a lot of guys who got his freebies, but also went to prostitutes, but the truth is it was never too satisfying. By this, I mean the enjoyment apart from the orgasm—it was "Well, here I am, do something." Or: "I'm doing this because you're here and expect it"—and nothing else. The bad thing was, whether or not I paid—it was never a thing that happened because both sides wanted it to happen.

But you—you saw people, both men and women, who gave you an appetite for intercourse! I was once married —I'm only 32—and I really wanted sex with my wife most days, but she was truly satisfied, I feel, with sex "once in a while." At least that was her expression. We had one child and a divorce. That was our marriage, in a nutshell.

She's now going with a lawyer she dated off and on before we got married—he's divorced, too—and I take care of the kid a lot and think a lot.

I am of medium build and not bad-looking. Blond hair, brown eyes and fashionable threads. I read the men's magazines and try to keep really up-to-date on the clothing styles. Gets me some side glances when I go out on the town with some lady.

My interest in you is realistic, I feel. I know we probably can never meet. But if you could just give me some advice, I would be really grateful. I know I must be at fault in some ways, but I really don't see why sex isn't a lot better for me.

Sincerely,

Bruce P. Hale

East St. Louis, Ill.

145

Dear Xaviera,

I may never meet you, but after carefully reading your book, I sure would like to.

My life is not one you could make an adventure story of. As a matter of fact I am thirty, a vegetarian and somewhat ascetic. But! I have an overwhelming yen for women. If circumstances permit or Providence orders a trip to New York, your calling card would be an ace in my pocket.

Thank you for listening—and again I would love to meet you.

Phillip T. Owens

Orange, Conn.

Dear Miss Hollander,

I don't know exactly where to begin. Maybe the best way is to first tell you a little about myself.

I am 25 years old and have been married for seven years. I have four children. I go to college part-time and hope to eventually become a teacher of English literature.

I am 5 feet 5½ inches tall and weigh 125 lbs. My chestnut brown hair is shoulder length and most people find me fairly attractive.

What I did want to tell you about is a little different and difficult for me, so please be patient. I'll get it out sooner or later.

Three years ago I had a nervous breakdown. This was from trying for so many years to hide something, not only from others but from myself as well. I married so young for almost the same reason—out of fear. I was running away from something I just couldn't handle then and still can't really. But writing to someone as sympathetic and open-minded as you is a step in the right direction.

Even now I find it hard to confess to a stranger that at 16 I fell deeply and passionately in love with my gym

146

teacher. She was a beautiful blond Norwegian, 22, with a very free soul. Nothing ever really happened between us. She took good care of me through the rest of school. I was alone and she cared for me, but not in the same way I cared for her.

I became so frightened by my own desires that I escaped into an early marriage. My husband is a very good man and in my own way I love him very much. But as hard as I've tried, I cannot love him as a wife should love a husband.

Even though she now lives in Norway, Johanna and I are still the best of friends. We write to each other as often as possible and she visits us every Christmas.

I have never had what you would call an affair with a woman and I doubt if I ever will. It's not that I wouldn't, it's just that there must also be love.

Your book taught me that I am still capable of feeling. I have never met you, and since you are no longer in the country I probably never shall. Yet I would like to more than anything else in the world. While reading "The Happy Hooker" I grew very fond of you. Not because of what you do but—I don't really know why. Maybe because you represent the answer to my whole life's yearnings.

Nothing would please me more than to hear from you, although I know there is nothing you can do to help me. I just want desperately to hear from you and get to know you, even if only through letters. I know that you can understand how I feel. If I didn't think so, I would never have told you all these things about myself.

Thank you for listening, and please please answer if you can—even if it is only a few sentences.

Sincerely,

Mrs. Inez Marino
Hagerstown, Md.

Dear Miss Hollander,

On page 184 of your very informative book, you discuss the problem of premature ejaculation in men. You mention a secret way to delay this by the use of a tube of "Detane."

What is Detane? Is it purchasable in the U.S.? Why is it a secret? Would you mind telling me in detail how it is used, where I can buy it, etc.

Thanking you in advance.

Kenneth James

Boston, Mass.

Dear Xavier

I'm really beginning to wonder about myself. I'm 17 years old and I get terribly excited looking at myself. I've heard of people being heter, homo & bisexual but never physically in love with themselves.

I'm presently going out with a guy of 20. Before him I went out with many men ten years older than me and I never had an orgasm with any of them except my present boyfriend.

But many times I would rather get dressed up in an erotic fashion, wear heavy make-up and masterbate while looking at myself in a mirror. Do you think this is a substitute for a homosexual relationship? I have always gotten turned on by pictures of girls and like to remain friends with boys while girls kind of scare me. What do you think?

Pat Runnels

Pueblo, Colo.

I think your book is gonna start a whole revolution in sexual thinking.

148

Dear Miss Hollander:

Having read your book from cover to cover, and back again, I must say that except for your disappointment in those with whom you fall in love, and the legal difficulties you encounter from time to time, the book is a most happy occasion. Your photographs cause me to wish I was your friend and to have participated fully with you.

How nice it would be if you had a house right here and I could visit with you and have the pleasure you could provide.

In Nevada, a few miles from Reno, there is a house of girls, probably the best in this entire part of the country. It's fully legalized, but doesn't have a classy madam, such as you were at your establishments. Most of them are young and pretty good-looking. They have weekly medical inspections, which is important.

The girls live right at the house and have, I think, two days off every so many days. Then they can leave the house, but while they're away they are strictly forbidden to do any business. In that way they do not have anything to do with rowdies. In that way they don't get into trouble on the outside, and they don't pick up any diseases, either.

Every customer at the house gets a short arm inspection before anything happens between him and the girl. And the girls are never bothered by rowdies or toughs. Two bouncers also live at the house. There are ten girls. It's a good system.

I sincerely hope good luck and pleasure come to you abundantly. You certainly have it coming to you, if anyone does.

All best,

George Phillip Munger

Klamath Falls, Oreg.

Dear Xaviera,

Congratulations! Your book is so stunning that for the first time in a very active life I am actually writing to an *author!*

The frank way that you tell your incredible story convinces me that you are warm, sincere, friendly, honest and outgoing—but above all, human. As long as there are men on the face of the earth with gonads, prostitution will exist and should certainly be legalized and prostitutes given licenses as therapists. I'm not kidding, Xaviera. You and your wonderful girls do more good in one week than the whole WCTU, Salvation Army and all those other sanctimonious hypocritics.

I swear to you that if it ever comes to a vote in my state (Michigan), that I'll go right down the line with you, and even campaign for legalized bordellos if you wish.

Keep 'em flying!

All the best,

Col. M. J. Foster (Ret.)

Menominee, Mich.

Dear Xaviera,

At first I thought your book was a complete fake. But then I realized that the only fake was myself. You got to me. You turned me on. Period.

Look, I'm hetero and I dig balling guys, but . . . well, now I'm *really* open-minded.

I'll be in New York real soon. I hope I catch up with you.

Yours warmly,

Loretta

[no address included]

150

Dear X,

I have written you four times and I sent you a box of candy as well. I hope you got them and enjoyed them. I hope the candy didn't get smashed in the mails—I packed it myself to avoid that.

I am 35 years old and happily married with two kids. I live in Des Moines, which is not the most exciting place in the world to live, but it's a nice family town and we like it real well. I read in the *Register & Tribune* that you are going to be in Chicago on Sept 11-13. I still have a few days coming on my vacation, so I think I can get to Chicago when you are there. I hope we can meet, at least for a few hours.

The thing is, I have this overwhelming passion to meet you in the flesh. It's not just that I'm after sex, but I would like so much just to stroke your long blonde hair and maybe kiss your body, if you'd let me. If we do go "all the way," I would pay anything you ask. Nor would I consider you a prostitute, because I know you gave up that life. I would consider you a kind and understanding and honest woman who wants to help a man who is tormented by desire.

I want you to know that I am sexually normal, and have never felt this way about any woman before in my life. I love my wife, but she is just a plain housewife and good mother who hasn't had experiences like yours that make a woman the most desirable creature on earth. Yes, I consider you the most fascinating woman in the world, even over Elizabeth Taylor or Jackie Onassis. Or any of those stars and celebrities.

Since I read your book I seem to have no desire to do anything else but meet you. The other night my wife made my favorite dish—old-fashioned meat loaf with potato cakes—and I had to *force* myself to eat it. That's how much you've gotten into my blood.

If I don't get to see you in Chicago, I'll wait ten yrs if necessary to meet you. I read you'll probably go back to Holland to live and I'll find some way to go to Europe to be around when you might be lonely or feel abandoned or maligned. Then you'll realize how sincere I am about you.

With all the love in a bursting heart,

Lon Hershey, Jr.

Des Moines, Iowa

Hi, Baby. . . .

You were a doll to handle things that well.

It was a real good ego trip to read about the ball (and balling) we had in a best-selling book and not have to worry about some gossip columnist creep ripping off my identity.

You're a groove. Stay well.

Your favorite producer fella (I hope),

[name deleted]

New York City

Dear Xaviera,

I love sex and thoroughly enjoyed reading your book. It is thanks to you and many other humans who have recorded and publicized their own experiences with sex that I have been able to put some order into my own interpretation of sex and myself. If I am somewhat profuse in my reaction, it is also because somewhere on this earth there walks a Dutch girl, *"Miehe", ā qui je dois une fière chandelle et puisque j'ignore ōn elle poursait etre aujourd'hui. . . ."* "I'll just have to thank the next available Dutch girl—you!

Your story has been fascinating and very human. If you

write other books or articles, let me know—it will be a sensational pleasure reading you.

Sincerely,

Jeffrey W. Van Ness
Yale University
New Haven, Conn.

Dear Xaviera,

Your book "Happy Hooker" was fantastic. I read it and enjoyed it far more then any other book I have ever read.

In your book you expressed the opinion that prostitution should be legal, to which I fully agree. However I think we can both agree that in its present form there is very little chance of it ever being made legal.

The cause is not completely lost though. Have you read "Surrogate Wife" by Valerie X. Scott? If not, you should, because in that book is the answer to legal prostitution thru-out the world.

Xaviera Hollander as a Sexual Therapist would have never been deported. Xaviera Hollander as a Sexual Therapist would have never been even arrested. Xaviera Hollander as a Sexual Therapist would have been able to treat both the husband and wife for their sexual problems and might have even been covered by Blue Cross-Blue Shield.

While you were giving temperary relief to a few men and running every risk imaginable, you could be giving permanent help and sued the pants off of any fuzz that ever gave you a dirty grin.

Even now, with the right kind of assistance, you could start a school on sexual therapy and sell the courses by mail, covering both the medical aspect and the legal aspect. Although you may not have all the knowledge in your head to do this, anyone as smart as you are can get it.

153

I am considering such a course myself, to sell mail order. It would use some presently available sexual manuals as text books. A girl working as a sexual therapist would run none of the risks of a prostitute and could actually give services with great therapudic value.

A medical doctor would be needed in each sexual clinic for both legal and medical protection. However with the money that could be made, that would not be very difficult. The clinic could be in downtown office buildings, where the great traffic would provide ample cover for both the customers and the therapists.

The sexual clinic could be run in such a manner that no one would dare complain. It would also permit the operators to be proud of their work and profession. One day it might even be accepted as a necessary part of the community.

Respectfully,

Russell Warey

Ripon, Wisconsin

P.S. Lou Gordon is a bigotted rat fink, the way he treated you.

Dear Mrs. Hollander:

I have read your book and I found it very sensational. I enjoyed it very much. Before I say any more, I want to tell you about myself. I am 39 yrs. old and kind of handicapped, they call it cerebral palsy. But I do everything for myself, I dress nice and the only thing wrong with me, is that my hands don't work properly.

I have gone to quite a few prostitutes in my life because they're the only ones I can go to. Since I have been going to prostitutes I haven't got any satisfaction in almost five years. I have been reading a lot of sexy books, like you have written. I have seen a lot of sex movies. I want to be

154

honest with you and tell you the prices I have paid. I have paid between $50 and $100 a visit.

I wish it was possible that I could meet you in person, because I need loving. I know I'm not good-looking or as manly as Rock Hudson or Burt Reynolds. From the picture of you on the back of the book, you look like a very attractive and dynamic woman, and also beautiful breasts.

Before I reveal what I like in my sex life, I want you to read this letter and think about my situation, and what I see in a woman like you. Maybe you could help me to come to a happier sex life.

What turns me on the most in the life of sex: watching two women making love. I love to see that and I really enjoy it. Maybe you think I am crazy or something. I don't want you to think that I am some kind of a pervert. I like regular sex, too. I always like to see a woman dress very nice. I have great respect for you.

Some people don't think much about sex, just go to a woman and pop their nuts. There is much more to sex than that. Please think of my situation, maybe someday I will meet you in person.

I would love to hear from you, and for you to tell me your viewpoint on my situation. Please write me and let me know, and then I'll write you back and tell you about my sex appetite. I'll sign off now.

Yours truly,

William C. Colbert
Omaha, Neb.

Dear Xaviera,

This is a true story. And if you answer this letter, I swear I'll have it framed, because this letter is being written at the end of a month-long search for you.

After I read your really right-on book, I got it into my head I had to meet you. So every night, after classes, I studied microfilms of newspapers and the newsmagazines, hoping to get a lead on where you were. The only address I ever could get was for your old apartment. And that was months ago, so I was pretty sure you weren't there.

So I started writing letters to different people and offices that I thought could help me. But I didn't get any answers from all that. So some friends and I decided to go up to New York City and hunt you down. Or smoke you out, as they would say in my home town in Georgia.

We went to the one address I had, and there we met an arrogant doorman who refused to let us in. So later my two friends ran interferrence while I ran for the elevator, but the doorman was too foxy. So we explained to him what we were trying to do. He gave us some story that "all that happened years ago, and not in this building, but another one." Well, I was positive he was lying, so we staked the place out from 3 A.M. to 8 in the morning, with at least one of us out front all the time. But our efforts proved useless, so we all went home mad.

I just got an answer from your publisher saying that if I wrote this letter in care of them, they'd forward it to you wherever you are. I hope he did. So you can see that I really did try.

If you don't answer my letter, I have a whole new plan for finding out where you are the next time we go up to New York. Please don't think I was stupid, because I wasn't. I have had a lot of fun doing this, and met a lot of weird people.

Please write back, because I and my friends cannot rest easy until we have "smoked you out." Thanks for reading this, and please get used to the idea that Fate wants us to meet some time, somewhere.

Earnestly,

Davy M. Goldman

University of North Carolina

Chapel Hill, N.C.

P.S. I'm sorry if I have bothered you.

156

(Editors' Note: During the period of this grand pursuit of Ms. Hollander by Mr. Goldman and his bold confreres, Xaviera was in London, Amsterdam, St. Tropez, Malaga and other Continental watering spots. So while Mr. Goldman's physical quest was in vain, his spiritual quest was surely in the right vein.)

Dear Xaviera,

As I've now read both your books, I feel it's not out of bounds for me to write you.

I lead a normal sex life—actually a pretty good one, considering I'm divorced and obviously less attractive than I once was.

What I want to talk to you about, though, is my—I guess it's a hangup—on breasts.

Whenever I make love, women seem to complain that I spend too much time on their breasts. I mean, I get great compliments on how well I make love to their breasts, but I actually get complaints that I love breasts too much and am ignoring other parts of their bodies. But my experience has been that by the time I leave their breasts, they're so passionate that a few flicks of the tongue down below and they're ready. I've been able to make nipples grow to lengths no man ever dreamed of, and I've taken women with small breasts and made them feel they were Marilyn Monroe.

I know it's a hangup—I'd rather come between a women's breasts than anywhere else—but I think it's a healthy hangup and I don't mind feeling sensitive about the criticism I've been getting lately.

There's one woman—she had no *idea* about how long her nipples could be until I sucked them into full extension —and *she's* complaining about—she's a schoolteacher and puts things politely—my extended "foreplay."

Seriously, ain't this the shits! I don't mean to get vulgar, but it ticks off my ass to think these women aren't appreciating what it's taken me so long to learn to do.

Tell me if I'm wrong. I love a woman's whole body, but

157

it's tits is where it's at so far as I'm concerned. Is that dumb, or what?

I hope this doesn't sound intemperate to you. I am serious in asking your opinion on this—from your picture you seem to have fine breasts, and I won't comment on what I'd like to do to them—but I would like some support in my theory of love-making.

Yours most cordially,

Roy M. Carlswell

Bangor, Maine

P.S. Since I'm near the university, I've heard all the Freudion shit I can take in one lifetime. I did *not* love my mother, in that way, and in fact I heard my father say my mother was a lousy piece of ass. I resented this as a teenager, but then it didn't seem important.

Miss Hollander,

I enjoyed your book so very much it hurts me. You said to write in your last book, so here goes:

1) What happened to Larry?

2) Please send me a picture of you (head to toe) in a bikini, and sign it:

"To George

Love, Xaviera"

Or something like that. You know, on the personal side, but so I can show my friends. Also could you send a lock of your hair? Both are for my Famous People's Pictures and Hair collection.

Thanks a lot,

George Rainey

Richmond, Va.

Dear Ms. Hollander:

I'm 22 years old and have a lovely body and lately have been developing an urge to become a full-time prostitute. I don't mean to say I'm a part-time prostitute now. I'm a court stenographer and, let me tell you, I hear so much sordid stuff it makes me want to move to another country!

But that's real hard work and why not, I ask myself, get paid for doing what comes naturally! I'll still date and all, but I'd like to go into business for myself, because these are emancipated times and I'd like to make the most of it!

The trouble is, I don't really know about how to go about starting even a part-time business for myself. I see lots of men every day, naturally, but what kind of signals should I be sending out to them to tell them I'm "available"?

Being in court, I know there's a whole lot of horny men around, so any advice you can give me will be most appreciated.

Yours most truly,

Velma Joy Jeffers
Tuscaloosa, Ala.

Dear Miss Hollander,

I hope when you receive this letter you are as beautiful and horny as ever. Whenever I read your book I alway have wet dreams.

Right now I have a broken leg but when I get well I will hop on a plan to Canada to relive my tensions in your bed. I'm 5'9", I wight 165, I have blonde hair and blue eyes. I'm Latan-American. And I love Cunts.

I work as an accountant at a bank. I know a lot of swinging people, so we can swing together.

About the appointment, please answer me soon. I love you and your two books, their so HORNY.

159

I would like to do everything that's in the book with you *Page by Page*.

Please send me a picture naked so I can get a Hard on every night.

Your One and Only Love,

Raoul Figuerosa

Chicago, Ill.

Dear Xaviera:

We have a story you might enjoy. We greatly enjoyed both of your books. "The Happy Hooker" was very impressive, so impressive that my wife and I did something we did not think we would ever do.

We were on vacation in Majorca last January. I had picked up a copy of your book to read on the flight over. I liked the book so well that my wife just had to read it too. But the one thing that really stuck in my mind and kept running thru my head was the word "FREEBEE". I thought the word was very well used and it's meaning very understandable. So one day just before we left Majorca I drew a funny happy-type bee with the word "FREEBEE" under it. I felt it looked nice and told my wife I was going to find a Tattoo Artist and have this freebee tattooed on my bod.

Well, I found a Tattoo Artist in Palma, showed him what I wanted, and he told me to come back the next day at 11. My wife and I showed up at the Tattoo place on time and he went to work on me. I droped my pants and I had my freebee tattooed on my upper thigh. He did a real good job too. So good that the next thing we knew, my wife had her pantyhose off, her dress pulled up and her leg over the back of a chair wanting to have the same freebee tattooed on her upper thigh. She had to have hers a little higher up than mine because she is a stew for [deleted]

Airlines and it would show under her hot pants if it were as low as mine.

So, because of you and your "FREEBEE", my wife and I now have our own freebees. A great BIG thanks!!!!

And . . . if you are ever in St. John's, come by and we'll be more than glad to show you our freebees. How's that for openers?

Very truly yours,

Cyril Heavyside

St John's, Newfoundland

Miss Xaviera Hollander,

Being an amateur grapho-analyst, I would love to get my hands on a sample of your handwriting. Would you write something for me, anything at all will do, so that I can analyze it and tell you what you are *really* like?

Enjoyed your book so much, I was closing my pharmacy an hour earlier every night just so's I could get back to your Arabian night adventures. This meant a drop in my weekly gross—but it was worth it!

Thanks again,

Harvey Cantwell

New Rochelle, New York

AN ADVENTURE: THE DRAG QUEEN BALL

The following is a letter I received from Dick F. from Toronto in October 1972. I was in Toronto doing the necessary work to put the finishing touches on the manuscript of my new book, and this was a letter that had originally been addressed to my New York publisher. Larry brought it from New York along with my other fan mail.

What first brought this letter to my attention was that it came from somebody who lived only a few blocks away from my hotel, and obviously had made the rounds to find me. This is the letter:

Dear Xaviera,

I am an admirer of yours, and it has taken me a couple of months to get up the nerve to write this letter to you. I saw you last week on the "Call Callei Show" and I finally made up my mind to try to track you down. I went as far as calling Elaine Callei but she refused to give me your address and suggested the easiest way would be to write a letter to your New York publisher, which I did. I hope that you will answer this letter or if you are (hopefully) still in Canada, that you will call me.

No, I'm not a cuckoo, a sickie or a weirdo. I do, however, have a different sexual appetite than the ordinary man on the street. I do like girls, and I'm not queer. I'm not a masochist or a sadist, but my one hangup is that I like to dress up as a woman. I also like to be ordered around by somebody like you. I saw you on this TV show, and I was quite surprised to hear someone speak so frankly, using whatever words were necessary for that part of the discussion. You really turned me on during this interview. I didn't think that people could be that honest on television.

I am 26 years old, an engineer of sufficient means, and I am not married, have never been married and presently have no intention of getting married. Xaviera, if you know what a true transvestite is, you know that I like to collect female clothes of all types, outer as well as undergarments. And you know how frustrating it can be not to have someone to show them off to. I would be very proud if you would pay me a visit and let me show you my collection. I so desperately need someone to relate to.

My telephone number is [deleted]. I end this letter with the hope that you will call me as soon as possible. With passionate desires, I remain

Yours desperately,

Dick F.

Somehow this letter intrigued me because of its sincerity, and out of curiosity I decided to give Dick a call. Also he was so close to the hotel that I felt it would be no imposition to have him come over, or for me to run over to his place. I did call him and when I got him on the phone, he sounded nice. His voice was slightly higher than the average man's, yet he sounded sort of groovy. It took him a few minutes to recover from the excitement he must have felt having unexpectedly received a telephone call from me. When he finally got his wits back, he invited me over to his place for shish kebab. I hadn't had homemade shish kebab for an awfully long time and the idea turned me on. I was curious to see what kind of man he was and what sort of meal he would cook.

So the following evening at 8 o'clock, just on time (Dutch punctuality!), I rang the doorbell of a lovely townhouse just off Bloor Street. After ringing, I waited for what probably was only 30 seconds but seemed like ten minutes, and a lovely young lady opened the door. She was tall and had long, dark, wavy hair, worn shoulder-length, with bangs. A multicolored knee-length Leonard outfit (my favorite designer) clung to her slim body. She wasn't voluptuous but she was still very attractive, with all her clothing accessories seeming to fit unerringly well together: scarf, earrings, shoes and perfume. She was wearing spiked high heels, and in addition to her make-up she wore long black eyelashes, which gave her eyes that mysterious Oriental look, especially since she had almond-shaped eyes. Her somewhat thin lips were almost invitingly made up to be kissed.

At first I was taken aback and thought I was at the wrong address. I looked at this lady and said: "Is this Dick's house?"

She opened her mouth, flashing brilliantly white teeth, and said, "Come in, darling. It's me. I am Dick. Surprised?"

Flabbergasted, I took a step backward, looked her over again more carefully, and then walked in. I followed her inside, and when she took my hand in hers, her hand seemed to be even more feminine than mine. I was utterly astounded by this beautiful creature, never having realized just how beautiful "he" could make himself. I followed her through the hall to a large closet where she hung my coat next to several fur coats.

Since she was dressed as a woman, I asked her as all women do on first visiting a lovely apartment, to please be shown around the place. In other words, I asked for the grand tour. She led me into her large bedroom and showed me another huge closet filled with the most beautiful clothing—so exquisite that even I would have been jealous of her wardrobe. On the walls there were unusually long mirrors made into three-dimensional configurations, similar to those you would find in a boutique. This "woman," I thought, must love to stand in front of mirrors admiring herself.

She took me away from the closet to her bureau drawers. Opening them, she displayed some of the most beautiful lingerie that anybody would want to feel, made in France . . . ooh la la . . . but of course, and spilling over with red and black garter belts, G-strings, French bikinis with matching padded bras, stockings from white to gold to silver to black, dainty lace handkerchiefs and a wide variety of shawls. And then there was still another drawer with a large assortment of matching jewelry.

She only showed me a few of the drawers; she said that in the other ones men's clothing was kept.

She laughingly commented on some of the problems she had buying this underwear while dressed as a man, and how so many of her women friends must wonder whatever happened to some of their finest lingerie—how it managed to disappear out of their drawers when there were no other women present.

Dick then asked me politely to go back into the living room, and suggested I stop at the fridge on the way and pour myself a glass of orange juice. She would meet me in the living room in a few moments, she said.

About five minutes later, in walked a new Dick dressed as a man, without a wig or make-up. And while a lot of the features were still the same, he surely looked all man—an attractive man with long blond straight hair. A few traces of lipstick remained on his

168

lips. "Ha ha," he said, "tell me the truth: Did you prefer the girl who opened the door for you or do you like the way I look now better? You're a woman who likes both men and girls. Who did you prefer—her or me?"

I was silent for a few seconds, and then I admitted that if I hadn't known they were one and the same person, I probably would have dug the lady as much as I dug him now. He laughed and said, "Come, it's time for dinner. Let me get my apron, and then let me know anything that you would like me to do for you and anything you would like me to serve to you, for I am now your humble servant."

Masculine Dick turned around and walked into the kitchen. He still had a little bit of a giraffe walk. A few minutes later he came out carrying large platters of food that he set down on the table. We were to have a full meal, from appetizer and salad to the main course of flaming shish kebab.

The living room was tastefully furnished, the furniture contemporary and bright. The predominant colors were black, white and red. There were several abstract paintings on the wall and some far-out lamps, some of which had sexual symbols in them, which immediately caught the eye. There were also quite a few art objects, tasteful pottery and many fascinating bowls and vases scattered throughout the living room. The thick drapes were of a red crushed velvet. A black-and-white chess/bridge table had been set up in a corner, with all the pieces fitting into the squares.

Dick came from Chicago, he told me over our appetizer course, and had only been in Canada for the last ten months, having been transferred there by his firm. He didn't know many people in Toronto and was very happy that he had found me, someone whom he could confide in, dress up for and, most important, relate to. He lived with the perpetual fear of being found out, so that he always kept his bedroom door locked.

"Dick," I asked, "how many people know you are a transvestite?"

"One is my jet-set mother," he said, "who I feel very

attached to. She is a lovely woman, and she brings in all the latest European fashions. She suffers a great deal because she knows that I suffer. She was my first audience. Amazingly, my mother wore the same clothing size I did and, once she knew, she let me borrow some of her garments. As a kid, when my mother would go out, I would sneak into her bedroom and try on her clothes in front of her mirrors. When she returned unexpectedly one day, she caught me in the act. She took me to see a psychiatrist, but in spite of running up big bills, those sessions never helped me. Fearing the embarrassment that could be created in a small town, she decided to let me continue with my quirk, but strictly in private.

"The only other people who know about it are two ex-room mates back in Chicago, but I don't see or speak to them anymore. That's where my frustration begins. The problem is that here I am in this lovely—but unfamiliar—country with this great urge to show off to the world how wonderfully I dress, but I have nobody I can show off to for fear of being ridiculed or even arrested. I would love to meet people dressed as a woman; I would love to go to gatherings and parties where people would never know I was really a man. You know that I like girls, that I really dig making love to girls. But what girl can I ask to let me take her along as my date, unless she is a lesbian?"

By now Dick had a distressed look on his face. We had both stopped eating and my food was almost cold; for that matter, I had become so intrigued by his problem that I had only partially eaten the shish kebab. "Dick," I said cheerfully, "let me think about your problem, but first let's finish eating. It's a pity to let good food like this go to waste. Let me think about it. I might come up with a good idea."

For the next five minutes the only sounds were those of knives and forks clicking against our plates. Once we had finished dinner and Dick had washed up, we sat down on the thick white rug in front of the open fireplace in the living room. Dick gave me several fluffy pillows and we were both lying on our backs staring at the ceiling.

Suddenly I had an idea. I said, "Dick, I have a great idea."

Dick was all ears, as they say. He raised himself onto his elbows, planted a kiss on my lips and enthusiastically said, "Precious, tell me about anything you have in mind. You turn me on, and I think I would like to fuck you."

I said, "Come on, Dick, forget about nonsense like that. I really have an idea. You know, you don't even know your own city, and I've only been here a few months and I do . . . Do you know what's coming up on the 31st of October?"

"What? Some national holiday?"

"No. Something like that, though——the 31st is Halloween, the day of masquerade parties throughout the world. You know, the holiday when the kids go around for 'trick or treat' and everybody dresses up."

"Of course I know. What do you want me to do——get dressed in masquerade and go up and down the street ringing doorbells? Do you want me to paint my face black like the kids do?"

"No, you silly. Don't you know that there is a great Drag Queen Ball in Toronto every year?"

"What?"

"Yes," I said, "a Drag Queen Ball, right here in Toronto."

"You know, I think I once saw an Andy Warhol movie that was all about such a ball . . . I think it was called 'The Queen.' That was a way-out movie! I remember all those guys dressed up like beautiful women. I would love to participate in such a ball but how can we go about it?"

"Leave it to X," I said cheerily. "I'll straighten it out. Just leave it to Xaviera. My only problem is that I've been invited to attend by a lovely young man who is, however, pretty square and I'll have to work that out somehow . . . What's today's date?"

He looked at his watch and said, "The twenty-sixth."

"Well, it gives me five days to make the arrangements, but I'll manage . . . whatever. I'll call Martin, this friend of mine—he's a TV program producer. And I'll make some arrangement.

"Dick," I said, getting up, "thank you very much for a smashing meal. It's getting late. Leave this to me and I'll get back to you in a couple of days, but you can rest assured that you'll be going to the Drag Queen Ball, and not simply as a guest. Somehow I'll work it out so you can go as a participant."

He seemed a little awestruck at this possibility.

"Forget about any other scenes, any scenes with me, I mean. Let me concentrate on getting you in with a lot of people like yourself, so you'll finally be happy. You'll be 'going public . . .' Ha ha. Don't worry—I'll get Martin to escort both of us, and maybe I can even arrange to get myself selected as a judge. I'll get in touch with you the day of the ball and help you choose your most gorgeous wig and a stunningly eye-catching dress and matching coat.

"Let me say good night to you now. I really must go. The food was excellent, really smashingly good. Thanks again for inviting me."

"Wait a minute," Dick said. "Let me walk you home." A moment later he reappeared wearing a very dashing man's fur coat. As we walked to my hotel arm in arm, he told me that while sex is important to most people, including himself, sometimes a good conversation took the place of sex. And in this instance, he had had one of the most enjoyable evenings of his life, he said, even though there was no sex whatsoever involved.

"You have no idea how happy it makes me feel to finally have found such an understanding young lady," he said with gratitude.

When we arrived at the hotel, he kissed me on the cheek and as he was leaving, said with a wide smile on his face, "I'm hoping to join you at the fabulous Drag Queen Ball."

172

Over the next few days I made arrangements with Martin, for both of us to escort my new friend Dick to the ball. Of the many people I knew in Canada, Martin, a smart young man of only 24, had been not only a good friend but also a fantastic fuck and a great, great suck. At first, he didn't seem to be too turned on by the idea of taking a transvestite along. But gradually he got used to the idea, at first merely tolerating it but finally being rather amused by the thought of the strange trio we would make.

Called "The Mad Gay," the ball is given at midnight on October 31st in a big hall or restaurant in downtown Toronto called Charlie's. The day before, I got together with Dick and was his only audience as he paraded all his beautiful costumes before my eyes. One was a soft pink ballerina's outfit, complete with pink ballet shoes, with which he wore his hair pulled back in a knot. Another was a gypsy costume, low-cut in front with big padded boobs. Looking like a takeoff on Raquel Welch, the overall effect was achieved with ample padding in all the right places.

Since Dick was supposedly not gay, he had not had silicone or hormone injections (although he confessed to me that one of his secret desires was to have breasts some day). He did admit that while he thought he had no use for other men, that once, while having sex with a girl, she had pushed a vibrator dildo up his ass and he had really enjoyed it. On yet another occasion, she had also rammed a candle—though a small one—all the way up his ass. He still remembered how much he had loved it, though it was slightly painful.

This man, I thought, though he apparently doesn't realize it, has very real homosexual desires. And being the queen he wants to be, obviously if I ever wanted him to go that far, he'd probably gladly assume the female role in a male-to-male sexual encounter. But wouldn't that be corrupt on my part? Not sure where Dick's head was at, I felt I shouldn't expose him to more new sexual ideas than he was able to handle right now. So I figured: let him play his transvestite game among similar-thinking males, and maybe eventually he'll still end up with an understanding girl on a steady basis. After all, he was a good-looking man.

The big night arrived. Martin, Dick and I set out for Charlie's. As Martin drove down the street not far from the entrance to Charlie's, we saw a long queue of people-watchers and passers-by standing outside, curious to see the drag queens getting out of their cars, mincing across the street and going into Charlie's. The crowd seemed pretty straight—adults and teen-agers —people who were just curious to see what was going on.

Like Dick, I was dressed in a beautiful long gown and was wearing a great deal of make-up. Martin looked great in his dark suit, very masculine and very handsome. In a reversal of the usual situation, he urged me to walk right behind him so I could protect his sweet bottom from any eager predators who wanted to touch his ass. Remember, there were drag queens all around us.

When we got upstairs, we had some trouble with the fellow selling tickets at the entrance. Dick, who looked absolutely stunning, had no trouble whatsoever, since we had a card stating he was one of the contestants. Martin had no trouble, either, but I was the one who had to pass a test. The bewildered cashier couldn't quite figure out whether I was a boy or a girl. While scrutinizing me carefully, he asked: "Hey, you belong here? Only men allowed tonight. Uh . . . aren't you a girl or what? You don't look like a boy!"

Though I was dressed entirely as a woman, I had my breasts covered so that no one could tell that I really had tits. I had made my chest kind of flat-looking. I also remembered to speak in a low, husky timbre, and when he repeated his question as to whether I was a boy or a girl, I whispered: "Darling, of course I'm a boy. I'm in drag, honey. Can't you see that?"

All of this was said with a seductive look in my eyes, in order to convince him I was as queer as a three-dollar

174

bill. Uncertain, he finally said, "Okay, you can go in. But remember, no ladies allowed."

As we went into a big darkened room with fluorescent wall paintings, I noticed that most of the males who had come as men were very masculine and muscular. But some who were accompanying their "lady" friends were dressed in grotesque costumes and wore powdered wigs. There were two dance floors, a small one and a big one, and there was also a stage where the drag queens were to appear later on during the beauty contest. Right now a male go-go dancer was on stage turning quite a lot of men on with his elegant movements. Between musical sets, he also served as a waiter. He was a beautiful, slim, frail, blond pixie, wearing very tight white hot pants and an orange-and-black tank shirt revealing a hairless chest. His long, shoulder-length hair made him look very feminine. He moved like an elf, capturing a subtle rhythm that you rarely see even in the best female go-go dancers.

Happily, we got a table close to the main dance floor. Dick, who truly did look fantastic for the occasion, sat with Martin and me and was enjoying every minute of it. He checked out most of the other contestants and seemed to feel pretty confident about himself.

He was wearing a long green silk gown, high in front, with long sleeves and matching long gloves. Very low cut in back, it almost revealed his delicate buttocks. The green gown was set off by a short, curly wig of flaming orange-red, glittering greenish-silver eye shadow and long brownish-black eyelashes. Bright shiny-orange lipstick matched the wig perfectly. He definitely made a much classier impression than some of the grotesque professional queens who, I'm sure, had appeared at many of these balls before. After all, Dick was a debutante coming out for the first time.

Dancing both with me and Martin gave Dick quite a kick. And even Martin, who is as heterosexual as they come, seemed turned on by Dick because he simply couldn't believe that Dick was a man—he looked **so** feminine. This was the proof of the pudding that Dick could have gone out in drag at any time and picked up men. But, as he had told us earlier, he didn't really like men, so the whole thing was strictly academic, if you know what I mean.

When I visited the ladies' room during the course of the evening, I was astonished at the sight which greeted me. Giggling and laughing, "girls" were primping in front of the mirrors, adjusting each other's wigs, eyelashes and brassieres—and zipping and unzipping their long evening gowns to repair "slippage." It was the funniest sight I've ever seen. And I especially had to smile when I went into the toilet area and saw that the seats were up instead of down, because these "ladies," despite their inclinations, obviously still peed like any other man does, standing up.

The show was to begin around midnight. We had gotten our table about 10 o'clock, so that we would be sure to have the best seats in the house. Restless as I usually get sitting for hours at a stretch, I suggested we go downstairs where there was supposed to be a small preliminary show at 11 for novice transvestites—"girls" who were new at the game and didn't quite qualify for the main competition on the first floor. At least that's what I was told by one of the queens on the dance floor. Passing before the peering eyes of the suspicious cashier again, we headed toward the stairs shouting toward him, "Bye now, sweetie, see you later. Just going downstairs to have a look." Then Dick and I, since we were partners, flitted close past the wary cashier, while Martin followed, nodding and smiling apologetically.

On the ground floor it was tremendously noisy and colorful: chaos first-class. I stopped Dick halfway down the stairs and said, "Whoa! Let's wait here before we go all the way down and see what's happening from here."

It was like experiencing an explosion of all the shades and colors of the rainbow at once. The dazzling wigs and hilariously long eyelashes were out-of-sight, and the multicolored gowns made of every material from silk to crepe to cotton were flecked with tiny gold and rhinestone sequins that winked up at us like little lost stars.

One queen was pillowed out as a very pregnant lady. Two others were made up as startlingly realistic witches, down to the ugly warts on their chins. I noticed quite a few black and white pimps, straight cats accompanying their working "girls"—men who turned tricks with men as street hookers during the day, but were basically gay themselves. In other words, transvestites who worked as hookers, making money for their pimps just like real chicks. I mentioned something about this to Martin and he said, "Yeah, some of them fool the Johns and get paid to give a blow job, which is exactly what they want to do in the first place."

There were also dozens of lovely "ladies" in every possible flamboyant costume. A lot of heads turned to admire Dick, who was standing next to me on the staircase. Just as the parade was starting, I noticed three men among the onlookers, all approximately in their early thirties, staring openly at **me.** When they became aware that I had seen them, they quickly turned away as if they didn't want me to recognize them. My mind started working rapidly, trying to figure out who the hell they were. Suddenly I realized one of them was a Danish cameraman living in Toronto, who had just recently shot a television interview with me. I even recalled his name as I pushed through the milling crowd, down the stairs and walked right over to them. Addressing the man I knew, I said, "Jan, but how nice to see you here. How are you?"

Poor Jan almost turned white. "Oh . . . Xaviera," he managed to say. "I almost didn't recognize you. How are you?"

"Fine. By the way, I'd like you to meet my two friends—Dick, who is going to enter the beauty contest, and Martin, my lovely straight friend. Ah . . . tell me, Jan, who are those two charming young men with you?"

Still shaken, he glanced sideways at Dick but obviously was more attracted to Martin—who preferred to move out of the picture altogether. Then Jan said: "Oh, uh . . . meet Chris, he's from Sweden, and Ernst, from Germany."

First I shook hands with the gorgeous Swede, who was tall, blond, very pretty and semi-feminine, and then with Jan's balding German friend who, despite the fact that he was about twenty pounds overweight, wore a thick woolen turtleneck sweater, which bulged around his fat belly.

Hesitating a moment, Jan said, "Hey, Xaviera darling, don't get any wrong ideas about me. I really don't belong here. We are just here to have some fun people-watching. Since there's nothing in particular to do on Halloween . . . that's what brings us here. Don't think I'm gay or anything like that, for Chrissake."

I smiled at him, then looked at Chris, who meanwhile had slipped around me to the other side and was now whispering in my ear: "Honey, he is just giving you a big story. Don't tell him I told you, but he and I have been roommates and lovers for the last ten years. We met in Europe, actually on the gay beach at Zandvoort in your gorgeous country, and came over to Canada together . . . Wait till he loosens up a bit a little later on."

With those words, Chris excused himself and chased after a robust-looking young fellow in his early twenties. Jan followed every move his lover made.

Once the ice was broken and Jan finally confessed the truth about himself, I promised not to get him into trouble and not to write about him (under his real name, that is). Everybody was in a terrific mood and Jan was pretty excited about my new friend Dick, but both Jan and Chris got turned on to Martin because they liked the boyish, innocent, straight look on his face. I whispered in Jan's ear that I would love to convert Martin, so we could all suck his cock. (I dig watching two men perform "69.") I was in that sort of mood, I explained, and could he try to bring it about?

Earlier that evening, Martin had already confessed to me that he felt very peculiar being the only straight guy in the group. He was also a bit uptight about being recognized by someone from the TV world he worked in, and he was anxious to avoid gossip that he might be gay. Word spreads rapidly in the world of the arts. On the other hand, while most men in the place didn't want to be recognized by anyone except their close friends, they also realized that anyone else who was there who didn't really belong would hesitate to comment to any outsider, for fear that he himself would then be a target for similar gossip.

Jan and I were by now very easy with each other and he suggested that we all go back upstairs because a) it was getting too crowded, b) too smoky, c) too hot, d) too noisy and e) it was time to see the big show. As it turned out, Jan had a table reserved upstairs. We all went back up to find that the dance music had just about come to an end.

Before the music stopped, I looked around carefully at each table and I was amazed to see at least three more familiar faces that I recognized from straight social affairs I had attended. These were people I had thought were the epitome of so-called respectability; but here they were, sitting at these tables, part of the crowd. And Martin was right; those people felt very uptight that I had spotted them. I simply didn't care about their uptight attitudes—I myself couldn't care less what anyone thinks or says about me.

It was now midnight and the disc jockey stopped playing his wild music. The gay Master of Ceremonies began with some humorous banter that most people ignored before he announced the names of the contestants. Dick, who had simmered down, now showed signs of slight nervousness. He simply couldn't sit still and kept moving around and got very fidgety.

Some of the contestants were really very funny. One of the girls called Abby looked very nice and sexy, really a turn-on, but when she spoke into the microphone on stage she became very shy and bashful. Another fascinating one had long kinky-curly hair down to her waist and was dressed in a black leather miniskirt, high

179

boots and a T-shirt. When she stood still, you could see the T-shirt had "FUCK" written on the front and "SUCK" on the back.

When the M.C. asked in a very high feminine voice, "Darling, what's **your** name?" the answer was "I'm a hippie chick." The M.C. said, "Let me see you do your **thing,** baby." "With what?" the hippie chick asked. The M.C. promptly handed her the microphone. As she took it, her painted nails flashing green, she whispered lasciviously, "I've had bigger ones than that."

Titters of laughter.

A moment later she looked at the M.C. in feigned shock and shouted loudly and clearly, "Hey, honey, your fly is open!"

Smiling, the M.C. said, "Look, dearie, what are you trying to pull on me? Are you trying to influence **me?**" The crowd seemed to love any unexpected or improvised line, especially if it was on the lewd side.

Then there was a girl called Michelle who had participated, she said, twice before. As she grabbed the mike to say some farewell words, the M.C. pretended to be scandalized. "Darling, what are you doing?" he asked, playing to the crowd. "You're not trying to swallow the microphone, are you?"

Michelle rose to his cue. "Sweetheart, that's all I have tonight," she said mock-forlornly. Then, just as abruptly, her expression changed to a kind of mock-radiance. "Oh darling," she whispered, "I guess I'm just an incurable cock tease."

The contest's low point was a girl called Astra, which means star, but she really looked more like a piece of shit than a star, unless it was a fallen star. She could easily have passed for a two-bit whore, and the audience whistled her off the stage pronto.

Still another one, Anabelle, was from Montreal, French accent and all. She must have had the longest and thickest eyelashes I had seen all night——at least three or four layers piled one atop the other. She was wearing a fetching décolleté gown with a pair of huge, rock-hard silicone tits spilling out of it. She spoke very

180

slowly and affectionately and said to the M.C., "Sweetie, honey pie, can I put my cheek next to yours?"

The M.C. laughingly asked: "I hope you don't have any communicable diseases?"

Anabelle said, coyly, "Oh, but of course, **cheri.** Did I forget to tell you? I have scarlet fever, a very bad case." The M.C. came closer to Anabelle, who really was **very** pretty, and replied, "Turn around, baby, let's have a closer look at you from behind."

Anabelle, with her derriere turned to him, giggled: "Aha, I don't know if I go that way, honey."

Then there was the witch who sang songs from short cabaret sketches and improvised some odd dance steps onstage; the pregnant lady, who evoked hilarious applause from the gay audience; and the last was our Dick, who had changed his name for the occasion to Gwendolyn——Gorgeous Gwendolyn. With her flaming red hair and seductively sexy walk, she strolled up to the stage to the applause of a wildly enthusiastic audience that greeted this newcomer to the event. Gwendolyn, basically shy and bashful, in contrast to the "come hither" look in her eyes, seemed to captivate nearly everyone in the room. Since Dick had a fairly high-pitched voice, he had no difficulty in passing for a very stunning girl. Seen from a lesbian point of view, I think I would have liked to make it myself with her right there on stage if I hadn't known that she was really a man. To me, at least, it seemed strictly no contest, though I confess I might have been prejudiced.

Nevertheless, a small horde of drag queen contestants, huddling among themselves and making enough noise to sound like a nest of queen bees, hooted rudely as Dick returned to our table.

After what seemed like an absolute marathon, the five-man jury sitting in the front row of the audience decided who the winners were. It didn't really take them that long. The unanimous choice for first place was——our very own Gwendolyn! I was afraid Dick would break out in a sea of tears once he won, but victory was too precious to him to throw away. Watching him, I was reassured that this triumph would crown his new career as a self-confessed transvestite—and also that he was on the biggest ego trip of his entire life.

After Dick was declared the official winner with much fanfare, Martin and I decided to sneak out the side door. We left our friends behind amid the tumult and the excitement of winning. But after all, I felt, Dick had about a hundred admirers gathered around him at the moment, and from among them I was pretty sure he would make many new friends, friends who would understand his until-now suppressed desires.

A few days later, Dick called to thank me for the "wonderful, wonderful" evening and, more important, for being instrumental in his making so many new friends. It had been a liberating experience in **more** ways than one, he hinted. Giggling into the receiver, he confessed that one of the boys had really turned him on, and that he was now willing to try a boy for a lover, something he had often thought about but—together with his transvestite complex—had always put away in the back of his mind.

I told him how happy I was that he had found a new life, and rang off by saying: "Whether it turns out to be Dick-Gwendolyn or Gwendolyn-Dick, goodbye and good luck."

*   *   *

Xaviera

Hi, I have read "The Happy Hooker," it's the best book I have ever read. It wasn't your episodes that impressed me so much, it was you, yourself, you seem like a really great person.

Before I go on with anymore of this letter I better tell you who I am and a little bit about myself. Well: my name is Dolly, I'm 15 years old, long red hair, blue eyes, 5'2", 120 lbs.

To get down to business, why exactly I'm writing you.

I have gone out with a lot of boys and done a lot of things so boys aren't my problem, but girls are. I really want to make it with some girl (no one special at the moment) but I don't know how to go about doing it, that's where I thought you could help me.

I have never done anything with a girl before so I'm scared that I'll be turned right off. None of my friends are like that so their out anyways. I'm not interested in girls my own age. I like them between 19-30 also it depends how they look and act.

I'm no butch so don't get me wrong about the whole thing, I'm really scared and I need your help. The other day I was caught in an electric storm in a car with the aunt of one of my friends. Well: we were both scared and hugged each other and I even got my hand under her skirt and up to her panties. But if she enjoyed it she certainly didn't show it. And I didn't know what to do, except I couldn't take my hand away until the storm was over.

If your not too busy I would really like to meet you. I have a lot more I want to say to you, but I'll wait and see if you answer this letter first, please try. . . .

Love,

Dolly Perrotta
Keene, New Hamp.

Dear Xaviera Hollander,

I must compliment you on your book, "The Happy Hooker." I enjoyed it to the max! It was rather educational and exciting.

My conception of prostitution was low. I used to think it was immoral, but now I look at it as an essential means of alleviating loneliness.

It would be far-out to meet you, or some of your girl friends who think like you do. I have no idea if this letter will reach you or not.

So if it isn't too much trouble just drop me a line. At present I'm stationed with the U.S. Army in Ansbach, Germany. My address is:

Sgt. Fred Lapidus

APO 798

New York, N.Y.

Dear Xaviera,

I don't usually write to people who don't know me but this time I have to make an exception. I came to Canada about eight years ago from Europe, so we are practically neighbors. During the thirty years of my life I have come to know people, to evaluate people. You are an exceptional person, a rare person in a world full of ordinary mortals. I have read your book and seen you on TV and I know this is a fact.

Speaking plainly, I think you are a fantastic girl. I don't think many people have your honesty and courage, that is one thing. Another is that you are really doing good work that is genuinely needed, that's for sure. I can imagine how many people write you angry or nasty letters, or threaten you because you speak frankly on a subject we all know is true.

At times you seem almost unreal, "too good to be true." But I know you will meet a man who will love you and you will love him, an exceptional man, as you say in your book. I should like to shake his hand, for he will be a lucky fellow and honored to marry you. Actually, I think I should be jealous of him, but I won't.

Your life will change now and you'll be very busy and life is not easy every day. You may get melancholic or depressed, and feel that you are alone or that nobody needs you. Life can take many turns. I am only a poor photographer trying to make a living and cannot offer much but I want you to know that there is somebody in Winnipeg who cares.

I am not trying to establish this sort of contact just to satisfy my ego. I simply like you very much and want to do something for you. I don't care what you have been or done—beyond that I see someone else, and this letter is for the real you. If you need anything, you can call, write or simply come. My studio is your castle.

Best of luck and I will be keeping my fingers crossed for you.

Frank Kieffer
Winnipeg, Canada

Dearest Xaviera,

Can you help me?

I love sucking cocks—if they're the cocks of guys I'm balling—and after seeing that silly movie, "Deep Throat," I have to admit to an enormous desire to be able to swallow cock like that silly lady.

As a film, I was hoping it would be really funny, but I have to admit I got turned on as Linda enveloped one joint after another. God, can that woman suck cock!

What I want to know from you is your own ideas on how to suck cock and whether you think my interest in this idea is reasonably normal. If some guy I didn't really know came up to me and flashed his hard cock, I wouldn't want to suck on it, but if it's a date of mine, I can't wait to stuff it in my mouth.

There are things I want done to me, but I do love this part of sex. Please advise,

Virginia Billingsley
Vancouver, British Columbia

Dear Xaviera,

Just curious if this will reach you personally. I am considered broad-minded and a World Traveler but your books make me feel like a virgin.

The ones who really go ape over your books are the ones who wear the masks of being the goody-goody nicey-nicey types. The ones who'd love to do it all but haven't the guts to drop their hypocritical masks.

Happy Hooking,

Mrs. Jocelyn Clarke (Under 30)

Galesburg, Ill.

(Editors' Note: The following letters are two of a series of letters received from Mr. Amadeus.)

Dear Xaviera,

I just got into your book for the first time the other day. I especially enjoyed the part about the 17-year-old boys in Puerto Rico. Wow, what a trip!

I'd like to meet you. If you feel unsure about me, you might invite me to your place. Sitting and talking together is a nice thing in itself.

If you don't want to do anything with me, please don't feel obligated. If you do give me something, I would consider it a beautiful gesture.

Much obliged,

Ronnie Amadeus

Hasbrouck Heights, N.J.

186

Dear Xaviera,

I haven't heard from you, so maybe I didn't tell you enough about myself in my first letter.

I'm no virgin, but I'm the next best thing. And I'll be 19 in May!

Hasbrouck Heights is a dead place. I am lonely, bored and introverted. Music is my only recreation—if you don't count masturbation.

Several months ago—before my first letter to you—I had my first taste of sex. It was with a 29-year-old married swinger whom I contacted through one of the underground papers. It took about five months worth of constant letters before I could finally convince her that it would be fun and exciting. And I was answering *her* ad! *She* was the one who wanted extra-marital pleasure.

Well, we finally got together and it was really nice. But our affair had to end because she and her husband moved to California. We did it in the back seat of her car, which was rather confining, and all in all, I only met her three times.

I've got to change my luck. I've answered so many ads already. I got lucky once. There's got to be a second time. I hope you're the one.

If you are interested in me, you have to realize that I won't be able to satisfy you physically as well as most guys, because I'm so inexperienced. So the pleasure you get will be more psychological than physical. It'll be different, and you'll probably like it.

Here's hoping,

Ronnie Amadeus

Hasbrouck Heights, N.J.

Dear Miss Hollander,

I heard you on WPLJ the other night and I became convinced that joining the house of a madame like your-

187

self would do me a world of good, both spiritually and financially. My situation is very similar to yours when you got started in "the life." I'm even the same age you were when you "lost it at the movies," so to speak.

My problem now is finding a good Madame who runs a clean, respectable house. Could you direct me to one? Where they have monthly inspections and all? I'm sure you'll think this is a strange request, but hell, I've been giving it away for free for years now—I figure about $50,000 worth—and it's time I started making it pay. Besides, like yourself, I love it anytime with almost anyone. Sometimes I have three dates in the same day and I ball all three of them. Separately, of course. (Even writing this letter is making me wet where every girl loves to be wet!)

I'd love to have a life like yours, Xaviera!

Yours truly,

Cynthia F. Miller
New York City, N.Y.

Dear Xaviera Hollander

I'm sorry you felt compelled to leave Amsterdam because it seemed too square to you, but let me tell you, baby, Amsterdam isn't square any more. Drop by Rembrandt Platz any evening and if you can't score some dope, get laid in style and in general have a high old time, well, then, something's got to be *wrong* with you.

This is—even *Time* magazine says it—the hippie capital of the world, and I hope what the papers say is true and you'll be coming back for at least a visit. Give me a ring and I'll show you an Amsterdam you never knew existed.

I read in your book you don't smoke or drink, but I

have nothing against just plain screwing for an evening. But I would like you to see the city you left for reasons of boredom in a new light. I swear I won't bore you.

"Hans the Great,"

Amsterdam, Holland

Dear Miss Z. Hollander

During your interview on radio station WPLJ, I called to make a statement, and to ask a question. I was the first caller.

I am a medical student, who has not been to a prostitute. Why? Because I have heard that most prostitutes are insensitive and just act as a recepticle for the penis. To me this would be very unsatisfying, since I get so much pleasure out of seing that my sexual partners are well satisfied. I do not think that I would find it pleasing going to a prostitute, coming once, and then leaving. Having sex in this manner seems incomplete. I have never enjoyed the "quickie," or the "nooner."

In addition, during the past several years, I have never been that "horney" to be in need of a prostitute. While I do not have a harem I do alright. However, there have been times when the idea of doing a prostitute is very appealing. But, I can't see myself going to Manhattan and walking the streets looking for one. A guy never knows what he might be getting into. Therefore, I have not taken advantage of the talent offered.

You stated that it doesn't have to be this way. Fine, but how does one go about procuring a prostitute that I might be interested in without spending $75-$100? I do not know of any of my friends who have bedded down with a prostitute, and I wouldn't feel comfortable asking my stock brokers, or my banker. I would appreciate any advice.

Good luck with your future books.

Sincerely,

James McReynolds Fitzwilliams
Teaneck, N.J.

Dear Xaviera,

I just bought "Xaviera!" and I'm glad you're continuing to write.

Your life seems to be so full of adventure and hope, and yet lacking in something that you are censored for.

Have you done something evil?

Would you ever consider doing something evil?

Do you know what something evil is?

The four color pictures of you on the back cover are very different:

in one you're glamourous (bottom left)
in another you are hopeless (top left)
in another you are bored (top right)
in the last you are temptation

On the cover you look like Elvis in drag.

FREE SECOND DETAILED ANALYSIS
OF THE PHOTOGRAPHS

Top Left: HOPELESS:—because you look like a weight-lifter; the picture shows a big arm.

Top Right: BORED—because of the drooping bottom lip and the get-it-over-with look.

Bottom Right: GLAMOROUS—because if I said evil, would you believe me?

Bottom Right: TEMPTING—somehow you look like EVE in afternoon attire popping out from behind leaves.

Cover: Your secret desire was to be a rock n' roll star. Maybe still is.

190

REPENT, SERIOUSLY.
REPENT FOR ALL THE $ YOU'RE MAKING.
REPENT FOR YOUR GOOD LOOKS.
REPENT FOR YEA KNOW NOT WHAT YOU'RE
DOING.

(My Secret Desire Was To Be Pope. However I must write more to be convincing and pray more to be understood.)

Guido Trafficante III

Plattsburg, N.Y.

Dear Miss Hollander,

My hubby and I just finished your book. We enjoyed it very much. The truth is, we read it in bed a lot.

You really have mastered the art of describing different ways of life that some people might find cheap and ugly without making it sound that way.

There is so much misery in the world. We learn of it each time we talk to people. Just a little happiness would go a long way with so many people in keeping them looking forward to tomorrow.

I hope you are well and happy yourself, Xaviera, and thanks again for a very enlightening book.

Yours, truly,

Ruby Sarr

Biloxi, Miss.

P.S. Sorry if I got a little dramatic there in the middle section of this letter. I really get up-set when I think about these things.

191

Dear Miss Hollander:

I know I shouldn't take your piece of trash so seriously, but I feel that you have defamed the American-Jewish man most seriously.

I defended my country during the Korean conflict and I am raising my children to be good American-Jewish citizens. My wife belongs to Hadassah, and I belong to B'nai Brith, and we both belong to CORE and ACLU. We don't have to apologize for our liberalism, or our sex life, either.

I carry a good hunk of meat around between my legs and I know, having discussed this with my friends, that none of us are sexually inhibited. I like eating pussy, '69', and any other combination of two people you can think of, and if you want proof of this, lady, then just invite me to come around. When you get this joint in your mouth, you won't be saying "Walla walla." And you won't be saying that Jewish-American men aren't swingers in bed, either!

Yours rather indignantly,

Dr. Meyer Zimmerman

Pearl River, New Jersey

Dear Miss Hollander,

We are two college graduate students who have just finished reading "The Happy Hooker."

What we especially enjoyed was your honest and straightforward style. But what *we* would really like to read is a book on "How to Please a Man Sexually" and we feel you are especially gifted to write such a guide for the mostly ignorant female population.

We would like to learn your techniques on such matters as how to capture a man's interest and keep it, how to keep your body fit for intercourse, how to stimulate a man sexually, the different sexual positions and how to manipulate a man into them without seeming obvious about it.

While neither of us is a virgin, sometimes we find it

hard to experiment, or maybe we just don't know where to start or how to proceed.

We hope you treat this letter seriously, as there is a great need for such a book for women.

Jo Hochberg

Sandra Winchell

Colorado College

Colorado Springs, Colo.

Dear Xaviera,

What a book you wrote! Reading it was like having my face suddenly thrust into a fresh, cool mountain breeze: most refreshing, pleasant and rewarding. I feel as if I already know you, although we've never met (pity for *me!*) but there is a reason, which I'll explain in a moment. I thoroughly enjoyed your communication (except for the jail scenes, and no one except a freak enjoys that kind of unhappy event) from cover to cover. Perhaps what impressed me most was your complete honesty and candor regarding subjects which cause most of the members of our society some degree of discomfort and agitation; is this perhaps because they fear the truth being uncovered about themselves? In this world of ours which appears substantially composed of deceit and lies, your book is a real joy to read.

And you! It's probably well that I've never had the pleasure of meeting you, for I'm sure I'd be hopelessly hooked by that beaming personality which shines through all your words. And instead of Larry, it would be me. But that's another story, one which hasn't had a chance to unfold.

Who am I? An ex-aerospace engineer, in and out of all kinds of menial jobs for almost four years, but at least I am still alive. The future always holds hope and promise. The most I ever made was 16 grand a year, and that went fast on a house, a wife, four kids and two cars. All that I have remaining is one of the cars and myself. I may cop-out to Australia and begin a new life there. My suffering has been quite different from yours, and yet I fancy that something links us together, something besides the usual male-female attraction. Perhaps our common denominator is the fiery insistence that we individuals must be permitted real freedom to express ourselves; I perceive freedom as a theme throughout your book.

If I'm a freak, it's subconscious, but I know I'm a real square; I haven't been liberated. I'm strictly hetero, on a one-to-one basis. Probably my strong, post-Victorian conditioning at an age when my intellect was naked and defenseless, but so far, I've been unable to shake these hang-ups. Here's where my strong rapport with you comes in: for almost seven years, I have been profoundly in love with a girl whose personality is almost identical to yours. You may find this incredible, but we've still never made it together, although from some of the rumors which are unmercifully tossed at me, I'm one of the few remaining whom she hasn't had. Maybe she's saving me for dessert.

What is so interesting to part of my mind is that regardless how many affairs she has, this powerful love from my stupid heart flows on merrily and unabated. I'm inclined to classify this one as the real thing, and not another infatuation. My complex emotional circumstances reminded me of some of the men you truly love. Could this be a trace of masochism in us both, even though on a subconscious level? I've wondered about it, and most likely, you have, too. Or it could be something on an even higher level, to which I've given some serious consideration.

In your epilogue you say you're 28. In four days, I'll be 45. *When* were you born? I'm an amateur astrology buff, and get some kicks out of doing charts, comparing with others and attempting to fathom what comes next. It's fun, and keeps me busy, helping prevent me from brooding over what good things I had in the recent past. If no one has done it previously, please let me erect a natal chart for you, and do a quick-and-dirty interpretation of what the

194

stars indicate for you (naturally, for amusement purposes only!)

You like to write. If you have time and are in the mood, I'd be flattered to become one of your correspondents. You have a keen intellect, so heaven only knows what kind of discourses we will conceive for close inspection and examination. I am quite skeptical that it would ever get boring to either of us.

Ever think about Reno or Las Vegas? The sexual crime rate in Nevada is significantly lower than in other states; it is illogical to believe that this is mere coincidence. The Europeans, South Americans and virtually the rest of the civilized world are practical and sensible: make it legal, set up controls, tax the hell out of it and everybody's happy. But we're like ostriches over here with our heads buried in the sand. Who are we kidding? When will we wake up? Anyway, you doll, I'm on your side, for a variety of reasons.

Thank you again for a fascinating and entertaining book. For the more serious-minded among us, it is quite thought-provoking, and I have high hopes that it will be the fuse resulting in an explosion of much-needed social reform in the specific area of prostitution. I only wish there were many more around just like you. *Viva La* "Happy Hooker!"

Sincerely and warmly yours,

James S. Maltese

Roslyn, L.I.

Dear Ms. Hollander:
In regards to two of your books,—THE HAPPY HOOKER and XAVIERA. I was very disappointed, after reading the first book and seeing your photographs on the second book. I expected a totally different looking person.

To me and many of my friends that have read your book you do not look at all like self description. You look as whorish and worn-out as any everyday prostitute. We really cannot see what any of these "charming" men can see in you—unless their descriptions are as false as yours.

Your "well put together" body is as really as ugly as one's body can get! There is no shape to it—nothing! Your pastered on make-up job hides what is probably an ugly face.

YOU ARE DISGUSTING!

Unsigned
Springfield, Vermont

Dear Heart. . . .

Thank you, thank you, for not mentioning my name in your tome!

It might have been ghastly for my career if you had done so.

Heartfelt thanks and a bouquet of hosanahs for your bright future,

[Name withheld by request]

Hollywood, Calif.

Dear Xaviera,

I just finished reading your new book, "Xaviera!" and I decided—well, I had decided even before I finished it to be truthful—to write you a mash note. I am not a diciplined writer or a diciplined person, so this will be a sort of stream-of-conscious-type thingy. I hope you don't mind. Well, to push on. . . .

I was feasting my eyes again on the gorgeous pictures of you on the front and back covers, and a realization struck me that, after the several lascivious flash-fantasies I inevetibly had about you and me, brought me up completely still: "That broad is completely, totally, *Utterly* alien to you . . ." And all the ways that is true came together all at once, right down *to* me . . . and my mind just blanked for a minute, disappointed.

Ah, but then, marvelously resilient as always, "Don't *think* about it." Writing you a letter is, to me, completely crazy, but I *want* to do it. So I am.

I'd love to fuck you. I've been trying to write that last sentence for the past half hour, and just sitting here. I tried composing it in a less crass, more genteel manner, and several translations came to mind, some true, some not. Finally, it was just that I hate pussyfooting. First, I would like to meet you, I think I really would. The rest is pure fantasy, it's relation to reality dependent on how we clicked, whether you sensed anything but drabness, but I'll tell you about it anyway.

I'd like to meet you. Just before we bounce or climb or slip or tumble onto the bed I'd like to pause, just for a few moments, and look at you; an excited, reverent, lustful, *interested* look. First I'd let my gaze rest on the top of your blonde head—well, not *rest*—the texture and varient shadings of your hair, then I'd let my eyes wander down, to your face, your forehead, your brows, your nose, caressing the lines of your cheek, mouth, and chin. Then down to your neck, admiring the lines and curves of tanned shoulders and down, lingering long on your captivatingly lovely breasts, softly supple, indented waist and smooth, silky hips. Down to your thighs, knees, calves, feet and toes, then, turning you around, up again, perhaps nibbling the backs of your thighs, touching you, caressing your back, up, up and around, up to your shoulders, your neck and finally, turning you toward me, holding your head in my hands, to kiss and kiss and kiss and kiss. And then I'd pick you up in my arms and take you to bed. I've just read this over and really, that's what I'd like to do. For starters.

I had some other things I thought I'd like to tell you about me, when I started composing this letter, but I think

197

that's all for now. I don't know if you answer fan mail, but if you don't or until you do, I may be

Yours,

Wesley Jay Campbell
Duluth, Minnesota

P.S. I'm going to mail this as is because I'd like to get it done, so please forgive the typos and spelling errors, where they may have occurred. It's 2:15 in the morning. Goodnight.

"Wes"

Dear Xaviera,

I was discussing with my wife the case of "German George" in your book, and one of my young sons—aged five—overheard the conversation and cited his knowledge of his favorite books, involving "Curious George."

"Curious George," in case you don't know him, is a funny li'l chimp whose escapades always end happily. They are real cute books and kids ADORE them.

Thus, I had this idea: why not use "Curious George" for sexual education manuals?

Ergo, these books:

"Curious George Meets the Happy Hooker"
"Curious George Learns About Orgasms"
"Curious George Plays '69"
"Curious George Goes to an Orgy"
"Curious George Learns About Bi-Sexuality"

Xaviera, you may think I'm kidding if you're not conversant with kids' books, but these would be useful books and, I bet, big sellers, too.

Cordially,

Brad Rayfield

San Luis Obispo, Calif.

Dear Miss Hollander,

I have read your two books (I hope there are more to follow) and your items in *Penthouse*. Thank you—very much for sharing. I may not say what I am trying to convey well—forgive me that—I think your books are works of art—equal to any Ruben or Van Gogh—they are treasures in literature also—equal to none on the subject of life—living—people—telling it like it is—really is—no "B.S." "Looking you in the eye" life! *Super, Super,* Great!

Keep it up please.

Thank you again for sharing.

Art Kimmel

Reston, Virginia

P.S. It is crazy—forgive me this one indescretion—but I would love to get inside your head for about two hours—gosh you've got a lot of good things there I'd love to borrow.

Keep Well,

"Artie"

Dear Miss Hollander,

I heard you on WPLJ Sunday night and have also seen you in *Time* magazine. I find you and your former line of work fascinating. I would like to work as a call boy (for women exclusively). I am hoping that with your connections you could find me a reputable madam so that I could be placed in a good stable. I suppose my hopes are a little high and you may think I am a crank but I'm really sincere.

I am Oriental, 5'9" tall, black hair, brown eyes, 145 lbs and have a slender build. I come from a very proper middle class background. I'm pretty good-looking and I have been told I have a very pleasant personality. Also 7½ thick inches. I'm not into sado-masochism scenes or perversions. Women like me and I like them. I guess you could call me a hippie. My hair has grown past my shoulders and my left ear is pierced with a gold earring. I am 22 and a sophomore at [deleted].

I would like to meet you to discuss my possibilities. I live on Long Island and can be there almost anytime to meet you in a bar or restaurant. I am giving you my phone number and address in all trust and sincerity. My number is [deleted] and of course you can call collect.

Thank you very much and I hope I'll be hearing from you soon so I can start my new life.

Sincerely yours,

Noel Chen
Lindenhurst, L.I.

Dear Miss Hollander:

I first would like to compliment you on your remarkable stamena and sincere honesty in both your books. It takes one hell of a woman to stand up to cruel public criticism.

I thought maybe you could help me with a problem. Although my sexual desires are not outrageously large, I do need it more than the average woman, much more. I am living common law with a man, and although he is very horny and very energetic, I just can't seem to get enough of it. Unfortunately, I become very much the bitch when I don't intend to be such. It is affecting my work, my home life and my relationships with other people in general. I feel that you could direct me or suggest some way that I may either curve or satisy this constant desire. I can hardly expect him to reach seven or eight organsims in one evening!!!

Please reply,

yours truly, horny and unsatisfied and very bewildered,

Fiona Gallacher
Pembroke, Ontario

Dear Miss Hollander:

I've just read your second book and it was fantastic!

I also read the first one, but to be truthful, I liked this one better. The first one covered your whole life up to a certain point, but then you seem to live just as exciting a life in less than a year.

I guess that's why I liked the second one so much. I never knew how exciting someone's life could be.

Both books taught me a lot, but I'll bet everyone tells you that. But being 15, and without *any* girlfriends, I really didn't know very much. Now that I've learned a lot, I wish I had someone to try it out on. Well, that's how it goes.

Yours truly,

Danny McArthur
Jasper, Indiana

Dear Xaviera,

I am a most avid fan of yours, having just finished reading your second book, and as luck would have us both residing in the same city at the moment, I was wondering if I might perchance become an ardent fan as well.

I am a very successful attorney and my girlfriend is the wife of a fabulously wealthy banker. Both of us like to swing (although not with our respective spouses), and I was wondering if we could invite you to join us in forming our own little daisy chain one day in the near future.

I hope your inclinations are in this direction, but if not, I'm still your avid fan.

With high hopes,

Milton Sahl
Toronto, Ont.

Dear Xaviera,

Please excuse my rather familiar salutation, but after having just finished your second book, I really feel I know you quite intimately, better perhaps, in some ways, than I know anyone else.

I need someone to talk to, and I feel I can relate to you. At least by writing, for I don't know how I would relate to you in person. I am almost afraid to contemplate that.

First let me say that I enjoyed both your books, the second more than the first because I felt that I was able to find more of your personality and the true Xaviera in it. How I wish I had but a fraction of your carefree spirit and emotional makeup!

Still, in both your books I detected a trace of loneliness—to which I certainly relate.

Even as I write, I muse at the irony of writing you. Me, a minister's grandson, former choirboy, whose own upbringing was so reserved and sheltered that it was considered a sin to go to the movies on Sunday afternoon, or plays cards, dance, and so forth. Hell, I never had a drink until I was 36.

I still don't smoke and my only lover has been my wife of 18 years. I've had a good life so far, blessed with a fine wife, two handsome sons and modest financial success, yet as I look back there were days when I would have loved to be as carefree as I wished—to do things for the sheer joy of the experience. But I never lived this way, alas. There always had to be some obvious purpose or deeper meaning to whatever I've done. I'd guess my background of self-denial still haunts me. I think it must.

My wife also feels this way about the past—that we married too young and have savored too little of life's experiences. Even after marriage, we were too inhibited by our families and background to really sow our wild oats together and just have some fun. How sad! How do you recoup 18 years?

Our real problem is what to do now. How to attack the future with the attendant responsibilities of raising our children. And above all, how to reduce the transmissions of our own personal frustration to our wonderful boys. God, Xaviera, how I long for some of that vitality for life you possess.

I've written far too much, I daresay, and I hope I haven't bored you. It's been therapeutic for me to write you like this, and if you should have the time to write, my wife and I would enjoy that. You're a terrific woman and even if we never meet, I'd like to count you as one of my friends. I know this sounds ridiculous, but sometime when you're feeling kind of down, perhaps I could help you like you've just helped me. And if you're ever near here, Marcie and I would feel privileged to have you as our guest.

Thanks again for letting me get to know you through

your books. I wish you the most wonderful and fulfilling life ahead, and earnestly hope you do find your Mr. Right.

With fondest regards,

Norman Hathaway
Terre Haute, Ind.

Dear Xaviera,

I have just finished reading both of your books and I can tell you quite honestly that *no* book or author ever turned me on as yours has or you, either.

I would like to have met you when you were in New York. You must have led a very exciting life.

I don't mean to imply that you may not be leading an interesting life now.

You know, your book kind of helped jazz up my love life—my girlfriend has practically worn me to a frazzle. My poor penis is grateful for the nights we *don't* spend together.

I'd like to meet you sometime—I really dig you. I'm sure my penis would get up (ha ha) for the occasion.

Yours most sincerely,

Walter B. Rozelle
Sandusky, Ohio

Lovely Xaviera,

Wow! I never thought that I would ever be writting to you but here I am.

Well, I'm 15, my name is Sibby Riccobono, I am Catholic, Italian decent, Brown hair, Brown eyes, I have gold rim glasses, I am crazy about your books. I live in Tarrytown, so if you're ever near here, stop in, my parents and I would love to have you for supper, I mean invite you to supper.

It all started last summer. My mother brought home your first book in one of those black plastic book covers. Well I went over to see the title and asked her why she would ever read such a thing? I said this because I know she isn't interested in sex any more. Anyway she said that it was on the best seller's list.

When she started reading it she asked me what one of the words were. It really said motherfuckin but my mother said mootahfuukin—you can see what she knows about sex.

I want you to know that your book taught me some, I mean a lot of things about sex.

By the way, when my mother finished the book, she said that she liked it. And I know she did. I read it twice and I loved it. I then gave it to my friend Frank and Gloria. They read it and gave it to some of their friends. I got it back and gave it to 2 of my friends, Matty and Willie. They love you too! But not as much as I love you—Oh yeah, an Uncle and Aunt of mine read it too! Then my Dad read it and said that it was eh! He said that he stopped after the first chapter because it was too dirty—but have no fear dear, he must have read it 10 times because you should see all the porno in his drawers.

Altogether about eleven people read that one book. I hope your not mad, I mean you lost some sales because of me.

I really hate to buy books because they're so expensive —but when I saw your sequel—I went right over and bought it. Without even reading the back flap first!

What I really like to do is to read one of your books on the bus to school. I like to see the expressions on their faces when they see your sensuous poster in the bus and then see me reading it. They make a smirk, nod to one another, ask me about it, say what these kids of today are reading (when they say that I spread my legs), sometimes the people next to me try and read it over my shoulder. I wish I had one of your book posters in my

205

room but I wouldn't want you to lose money on advertising because of me.

My favorite actress is Jane Fonda. Do you like her? She really is a Bitch—she even looks like one, but she is sexy. Anyway I want you to know that you're my second favorite. I hope you don't make a movie out of your first two books because you would degrade yourself. But if you should I hope you or Jane Fonda play your part.

Could you *please* send me an autographed picture of you? A real autograph? Do you think you would like to write me or visit me and my family? If so enclosed is my phone number along with my address.

If you should send me something in the mail (a letter I hope), could you please don't put a return address. My mother may keep it on me. You see they really do like you. I heard them talk about you but they just want to keep me away from sex.

My friend Andy said that he saw you at [deleted] at a lecture, I almost went crazy. I mean I whish that it was me and not him.

Xaviera, I have a real crush on you. Maybe I look to you for love or mother love, or your body—but I love you. I can't wait for your next book. I know I will meet you, maybe not face to face but I will see you. I read your column in *Penthouse*. Why don't you pose just once for *Penthouse* or *Playboy*?

Well, so long for now and remember me please.

Till we meet,

Sebastian (Sibby) Riccobono

Tarrytown, N.Y.

PS. I love to hear or see you on news. I can't wait to see you on eye witness news. I missed the times that you were on.

Dear Miss Hollander:

I have just learned, via the "Dick Whittington Show," that you are being forced to leave the United States. It's my feeling that this is grossly unfair to you as your grace and honesty has benefited this country's social scene.

If my protest or advocacy could in any way be of help to you, please don't hesitate to call on me for support.

Sincerely,

Herbert P. Goldberg
Olympia, Wash.

Dear Miss Hollander,

Have just finished reading your book, and I think it was written in good taste. I've given it to my husband to read now.

I have the utmost respect for good Madams, good call girls, but not for the 50¢ to $2 ones. My Father always told me that if a woman has a half way decent body, it should not be played with like a toy, and I'm in full agreement with his wisdom.

I would rather have a good call girl for a friend, then some of the so-called righteous females.

Perhaps sometime they will make prostitution legal, I hope so, and I am also for legalized gambling and abortion.

If possible, could you answer this letter and let me know what your birth sign is?

We have a 12-year-old daughter, and her name is Valentina, and pretty soon I'm going to let her read your book, as my husband and I are fairly broad minded people.

Again I liked your book, and hope you will be able to

return to this country to live. You could be Secretary of Sex Education or something like that on the President's Cabinet.

Sincerely yours,

Mrs. Jean Sable Goldsmith
Haddontown, Pa.

Dear Xaviera,

I am a 23 year old female college student and I have a fetish and I want to know if you have ever come across any other girl with the same problem.

My fetish is the boots that you see many women and girls wear. For some reason I just desire the hell out of any girl who wears them. It seems that every time I see a beautiful girl walk by I just think of all kinds of wicked things that I would like to do to her, from licking her boots all the way to the top of her head.

Mine is a very humiliating problem, and I would like to know what I can do to find other girls with the same fetish. Are there any tell-tale signs that a girl may be a boot or shoe lover?

Nancy Lammons
Iowa City, Iowa

Dear Miss Hollander,

It has been a great pleasure for me to read your two books: "The Happy Hooker" and "Xaviera", and I decided to use the opportunity of your visit to Burlington Mall to send you this note together with a bunch of flowers.

In my home country Denmark we always use flowers to express our feelings, and today I wish to express my sincere thanks to you for some most enjoyable hours while

208

reading your two books, and also my admiration for the courageous, witty, and—I am sure—very charming author, Xaviera Hollander.

I wish you all the best for the future and I am looking forward to your third book.

Sincerely yours,

Borge Hallversen

Hull, Quebec

P.S. If you should happen to notice in the crowd an average looking middle age man with old fashioned short hair cut and carrying your latest book and a Nikon F. camera, it could be yours truly.

Dear Madam Hollander:

I have been living out here in Arizona for way over a decade. I have been going to a house—woops, "house"!— in Nogales, Sonora, for most of that time. Just love that place. "No sweat" in getting the girls. But I've also found during the ten years I've been going down there that total satisfaction means regular sex rather than "so-called 69 or quickies."

I find that the more times I visit that "house," the more friendly the people there are. Since last Aug. 3rd I've been seeing a girl—she was new last summer—who normally charges $10, but for me it's never over $6! I gladly buy her a drink or two, but, then, I get drinks on discounts, too.

I managed to be born between all the wars, so you can't imagine how much I wanted to fight for *our* American nation. And you can't know how much I am glad to be an *American* and how much I *like good hot pussy!*

Had to wait three weeks to get your book. Been reading it all week. A real "HOT" book.

Many times when I go with a girl in the "house," the

girl takes a leak before we screw. I don't mind. I just say to them, "Don't blow your bladder." They laugh like hell —call me "funny gringo" or "crazy American."

Where did the old saying come from—"Don't fart when fucking"? Bet you can't guess!

Well, gotta go now. Write if you get work!

Best of all,

Charlie Scarne
Oracle, Arizona

Dear Ms. Hollander,

As a contemporary feminist and liberated woman, let me say that I deplore your sexist book in the extreme. Even the title is insulting to women, for it views them only as sex objects in a male-polluted world. That you should dedicate your energies to the degrading business of "pleasing men" deeply saddens and revolts me.

The female body is a very beautiful thing. That is why men are willing to pay exorbitant amounts to possess it, if only fleetingly. In my radical feminine caucus we have discussed whether or not a true feminist should give her body to a man. Some of us do. Speaking for myself, since college I have never slept with any man (though many have begged for it) and have only enjoyed free, uninhibited, totally equal sex with other women. It was glorious as a student; it is heavenly as a grown woman.

You yourself show some glimmering of awareness of this, as your relationship with Helga at the beginning of the book indicates. That was true love, and Helga loved you and if either of you had been free from male-dominated thinking, you would have run off together.

Mostly we resent your book because it has appeared at a time when we are involved in a live-and-death struggle with the natural enemy—man. You are giving aid and comfort to this hairy, insensitive beast whose idea of humor runs the gamut of men's room graffiti to Hollywood sexist comedies, always putting women down.

One day you will see the truth of this and abandon the "feminine" role assigned to you by men and find your true identity.

SISTERHOOD IS POWERFUL.

Sisterly yours,

Ellen Fairservice
Cos Cob, Conn.

Dear Xaviera,

I am 19 years old and a cadet at [deleted], but before you let that influence you, I'm not a military fuck or anything like that.

I listened to your interview on WPLJ Sun. night, and I enjoyed it thoroughly. I would like to tell you that you didn't sound like what my opinion *was* of a prostitute. You seemed to be a very intelligent woman, with a fantastic personality. I would love to meet you, and to tell you the truth, I would love to have sex with you, but, I know that that is just a little too much to wish for.

I would like to tell you a little about myself and ask a few questions. The first time I had sex in my life was last May. I was "seduced" by a 35 year old married woman, and I was scared to death. Counting Jan. 15 we have made love 21 times give or take one. So far she is the only one that I have made love to.

Last summer I met a girl that wasn't interested in sex, but I didn't find this out until about the third time we went out. She really liked me, but I didn't like her, so I tried to get something for nothing. Her lack of interest made me bold. I tried everything I knew but she just wouldn't give in. So I just quit on her.

Now I'm going with a girl that I really dig. I'd love to

have sex with her, but, I don't know why I just don't try. What puzzles me is the difference between the way I feel now, with this girl, and the way I felt with the other one. I was very callous about her, but I guess I really care about this one.

I thought maybe you might have some answers. You sounded like you had your head together with everything that might happen with love.

With all my respect,

Reginald Kasten, Jr.

N. Toms River, N.J.

Dear Miss Hollander:

I've listened to you a few times on the radio and have read your interview in *Screw*. Now that I've read your book, I wholeheartedly agree with your campaign, as you might call it, for complete sexual freedom and against outdated sexual laws.

I also agree with you about the average Dutchman, especially their stingyness—French girls told me this years ago—and I accept your word as far as they being not too good as lovers either.

I consider myself an exception to the proverbial rule, and I would like to have a farewell dinner with you, with lots and lots of good conversation. I've been here 18 years and never felt the urge to see The Netherlands again but went back last year since both my parents are getting on in age—my mother was 85 yesterday. Incidentally, if you accept my invitation, it wouldn't be Dutch treat and I won't insist on any dessert. . . .

Although I love spaghetti, I try to stay away from it but this is not my idea of a dinner date anyway, so you tell me what you'd like to remember me by.

I do want to tip you off about an arrogant bullshit artist who writes a so-called jet-set column for *De Telegraaf*.

This crashing bore and psychological sadsack has been writing vicious little items about you—I spent nine months in Holland recently and read all the papers every day, and knowing his kind of journalistic approach, I wouldn't be surprised if he were the first one to try to get in touch with you and "have" you in his column—he doesn't strike me as the type who could have you in any other way. He writes under the name of Henk van der Meyden, or something like that, which is probably not his real name.

I am 53, 5'10", 190 pounds, divorced and although the first and the last items aren't obvious, the rest will allow you to spot me immediately without my having to carry a rolled-up newspaper under my arm or wear a red carnation in my lapel.

As I have been back long, I am trying to get cut flowers in the supermarkets here, but it isn't easy. Nothing you really want in life is.

Hoping to meet you soon. Love and peace,

Paul Schocken

Newport, Rhode Island

My dear Miss Hollander,

I have read your book and I feel I must respectfully object to your comments about the smallness of the penises of Oriental men. Perhaps you are judging all Oriental by the waiters and cooks at the Chinese restaurant that provided you with free food.

Aside from Thais, some of the largest members I have seen have been on Oriental men, who know things about pleasing women that Occidental men can only guess at. (I'm sure you have seen some of our lithographs.) I don't want to seem immodest, by any standards, but I myself stand eight inches in length.

I would submit that the Orientals who passed through your portals were not typical of the Oriental male.

Respectfully,

Sessue Isaki
Hilo, Hawaii

Dear Miss Hollander:
My husband is positive there is something physically wrong with him because after making love, he finds that he can't produce another erection for a half-hour.

I've told him, over and over again, that this doesn't bother me at all because I would rather screw for thirty-forty minutes and be satisfied than to screw for five minutes and not be satisfied.

He never complained of this situation until one night when we were in bed with a close friend and my husband could get an erection any time he wanted one.

Do you have any ideas on this? Is it just a mental thing, or do you think it might really be physical? He's too embarrassed to go to a doctor, but maybe he should.

Sincerely,

Susannah Caine
Benkelman, Neb.

Dear Miss Hollander,
I've seen you on TV and I've read "The Happy Hooker" and I think it's great. I say you're great, Miss Hollander.

I know this might sound a little strange. After all, you have no idea who I am. But I believe my reason for writ-

214

ing is good and sound and there is something I would like very much to talk to you about.

I read how you have helped so many others and I was hoping beyond hope that maybe you would help me also. I was always troubled until I read your book, then I thought why not take a chance at least, so I did. I can't go into it here because it's something I would like to discuss with you *personally*. Please forgive the writing because I am all shook up just writing to you, happy just thinking that maybe you will write to me.

I am 25, single and black. I hope that doesn't mean anything to you. I would send you my photo but I don't want to count my chicks before they are hatched.

I hope very much that you write back because I'm very interested in you and your line of work.

Thank you,

Earlene Claxton

Kansas City, Mo.

Dear Xaviera,

I have read both your books and feel as though you are an old friend.

I know one person should never give another advice especially never having met that person. However, sometimes someone on the outside can see things you can't.

You write at the end of your second book that if you could find the right man you would be glad to settle down and have your sexual hunger fulfilled by one man.

The type of man you describe isn't impossible to find, but almost. Now that you have become famous and possibly wealthy, you could never be sure if he were marrying you for yourself or not. You have been taken in a few times already.

It sounds like you are looking for someone to come along and sweep you off your feet. These marriages usual-

215

ly start off with a bang (excuse the pun) but often end up on the rocks.

I guess what I am trying to say is that I think you will look a long time before you will find another man so well suited to you as your boyfriend Larry.

He has known you since before you became rich or famous so you would know he was not after your money. You also know his sexual demands or tastes wouldn't change like your ex-fiance Carl. He is concerned for your welfare and it sounds like you have a good relationship with him. He seems to be a good stabilizing force in your life. If he is free to marry you, if I were you I wouldn't let him get away.

I know you have mentioned that you didn't love him: Yet when you mention him in "Xaviera!" you sound like you have very special feelings for him. I refer to page 382, paragraph 2 and page 415. You describe your ideal man on page 286 in the last paragraph and that seems to describe Larry. On page 415 you say you need him like a nice safe harbor to get back to, but if you keep him like a dangling participle he won't always be there.

While I am writing to you I would like to ask you a question. You state that one of your favorite positions is 69. In that position the man and woman lie on their sides facing each others genitals. I can understand how the woman can reach the mans penis with her mouth, but I can't see how the man can reach the womans clitoris or vagina.

I realize you probably get a lot of letters but I hope you give some thought to what I have said and that if you decide not to marry Larry that you do find the right man and find happiness.

Just keeping in touch with the Dutch.

Mrs. Wilma Dow

Greensboro, North Carolina

216

Dear Ms. Hollander:

I enjoyed your books and wanted to tell you they're just great!

However, I really felt low in "Xaviera!" when you said you're more or less glad to be out of the business. I sort of know what you mean because I "worked" part-time this summer in a moment of desperation and I enjoyed the work, although some of those people think a call/boy/girls body is made of Herculon and can be treated like a piece of rubber.

But came the fall and I decided to go "straight," after some close shaves with the right side of society. Now I'm working the old 9-5 routine and I really hate it.

My boss—speaking of the "right side" of society—had the same problem as yourself, only they quickly shipped him on a plane back to Greece and now he faces trial there.

Hope things are going well with you and you're enjoying your new life.

Yours sincerely,

Charlie Winters
Manhattan
New York City

Dear Miss Hollander,

It's hard to concentrate on anything here with all the noise, so I was surprised that your book was so good! I am sorry my writting is not better so's I could tell you just what a relief it was to read such a sassy book over here. But anyways it's getting dark here and I am in a bunker. I am stationed outside Da Nang and it is a nice place but you could get killed because people tend to shoot at you

217

now and then. The reason I am up in the middle of the night and have been up for 36 hours straight is that Charlie is raising hell.

In the last week the VC has taken over a dozen fire bases off of the ARVN, which isn't saying much for the ARVN. We are practically in North Vietnam, being only 75 miles from the border. We are the closest American unit in Nam.

I just wanted to write and tell you that you've made the life of at least one GI a little happier with that zappy little book. Keep up the good work.

Yours truly,

P.F.C. Anthony Parsons

A.P.O.

San Francisco, Calif.

Dear Miss Xaviera Hollander,

I'm just a teen-ager who's 14 years old. I read the book "Xaviera!" in exactly two days, maybe even less. I never thought that such a book could be published. I'm going to start on "The Happy Hooker" right away. Doesn't all those things that you've done give you a bad reputation? There's a few things I'd like to know. How did you become a prostitute? Did you ever work at a boring job, like every day? How did you become so rich before you wrote the book?

You do quite a bit of travelling so I was wondering if you ever visited any schools or places where teen-agers could be free to ask you any questions which they feel could be answered by you because you've been through many sexual facts and figures. I was wondering if you would be able to visit my homeroom, which is also my french room. My school is called [deleted]. Whether you can or you can't come I'd still like to hear from you.

Thank you very much

Yours truly,

Billy Buchanan

Glen Falls, N.Y.

Dear Miss Hollander,

I just finished reading your book. And I am reading it to my husband. He can't read very good so I get the pleasure of reading the book again. My husband says that he doesn't care much for it. But he does. He's the type that won't admit to somethings.

You should be recommended for an award for the work you are doing. I myself think they should legalize Prostitution. Not the street walkers, but the madams and their houses.

My best friend is a prostitute and she has a pimp. (Well, I really should be honest). My cousin-in-law was a prostitute, my cousin was her pimp. Prostitutes should not have pimps, but madams who can run things a hell of a lot better.

I am 26 years old and I love my sex. I have made love to my girl friend twice and her husband was there also. And we all enjoyed it. I am not that great of making love to another woman. Since I first started going with my husband before we married and after I have had no relationship with another man or woman.

I better close so my husband won't see me write to you.

I wish you the best of luck in your life. And I pray to God that they legalize your proffession. It's not a sin your committing. Its the pleasure of nature for giving you this art of Love.

Yours Truly

Rowena Wyatt
Ashville, N.C.

Dear Happy Hooker,

I watched you on the Miss Callei program but couldn't get through the phones to speak with you about your ideas.

The reason I was calling is I have this one problem concerning sex. I guess hundreds of others have it too, but it is really depressing me. You see, I am 24 and still a virgin and though I know in some cities you can go to prostitute houses, I can't seem to locate any in Toronto.

I hope I don't sound like a sex maniac. I'm really not. It's just that everybody talks about it all the time and I would like to experience it at least once.

I've tried going to different hotels and drinking at the bar, but I never seem to run into that type of girl. Maybe I'm going to the wrong places. I love dancing and have gone to many dances where I have danced with many different kinds of women. But when it comes to approaching the subject of sex I turn stone cold with fear. One night I got the courage to ask one girl and she punched me right in the eye. In the morning I had a black eye. Try to explain something like that to your friends.

While all my friends my age are getting married, I am still living at home with my folks. Maybe you could recommend some books I could read on the subject that would help me.

Thank you for reading this letter. I couldn't remember

your name from the program so that's why I addressed it "Dear Happy Hooker."

Sincerely,

Harry Liss
Toronto, Canada

Dear Miss Hollander,

To start this letter off, I must say I have to be your greatest fan. My name is Jeff and right now currently doing a four year hitch in the U.S. Navy. The reason I am bragging about being your greatest fan is because most of my ship mates have beautiful nude girls hanging around their racks. I myself have seven pictures of you. The pictures of you are from the bustline up, and you are fully dressed. This little fact brings a lot of laughs and remarks towards the both of us. The trouble is most of these guys have not read and fully enjoyed your two books. And when I announced that I was going to try to send a letter to you they really laughed. I would greatly appreciate some kind of reply. I would just like to prove to a lot of people that no matter how crazy an idea a person may get the best thing to do about it is try to carry it out.

I am really sorry your life style was busted up in New York City. You see that is where my ship is home-ported. And believe you me I would have been more than honored to bring some business your way, to your girls.

If you should ever chance to be in New York again, I hereby extend an invitation to you to come and visit my ship. I'm sure everyone would be delighted if not shocked to death at your presence.

We are moored right under the Throgsneck Bridge along the East River. My full address is on the envelope.

Well I guess I'll close now, but please try to send some

kind of reply, if nothing else a picture autographed by you would do me very nicely.

Yours truly,

Jeff M. Stonehill
F.P.O. [deleted]
New York, N.Y.

Dear Miss Hollander:
In the three years I've been having sex regularly—I'm 18 next June—I've gotten no satisfaction really from normal intercourse. I'm in good health and really *love* girls, but it only feels good when I get a blow job or else a girl friend masturbates me. And then not any girl at all—it has to be someone I really like or else someone with a very delicate touch—but why can't I have as good an orgasm when I'm doing things the normal way?
Any answers will be deeply appreciated.

Respectfully yours,

Bob Tolliver
Casper, Wyoming

AN ADVENTURE: A FUNNY THING HAPPENED ON THE WAY TO THE TENNIS MATCHES

I received a strange kind of Valentine this year—1973.

It was around 3:45 in the morning, and I was just in that state between still being awake and nearly being asleep. And the damn phone rang—this was my Valentine message.

In a state of half-sleep-half-awakeness, I stumbled from my bed into the living room, where the phone was clanging away. I banged against the coffee table, gave a loud curse—which if nothing else helped to wake me up somewhat—and threw myself down on the couch, at the same time ripping the phone off the receiver. "Hello," I said in a groggy-infuriated voice, "whoever the hell it is, why are you calling in the middle of the night!"

A high-pitched voice responded, her words punctuated by a series of drunken hiccups. Some drunken, or at least semi-polluted, woman calling up in the middle of the night—I was not amused! "Hi, is this Xaaaaviera?" the voice said. "The Xaavierra from the book? I can't believe it—I finally found you!"

From my end, a groggy voice admitted that she had "finally" found me, all right.

She went on: "I am calling from Winnipeg, long distance, but that doesn't matter . . . Have you got a minute? I have **got** to tell you how I finally got ahold of you. . . ." At this point she obviously turned away from the phone and said something to someone. Probably: "Get me another drink."

Then her voice came back into the receiver: "You wouldn't believe this, but I am smarter than those dumb operators . . . I simply said I was a reporter for the **Free Press** and just had to find Miss Hollander, and

225

you know what——the Toronto operators really must've heard about you because after all kinds of interrogations from them, one of them finally called me back with a list of about ten hotels where you might be staying, so I just started with the biggest of them and in only six calls I reached you." She paused here, for some alcoholic refueling, I supposed. "Hey, Xaaaavierra," she then went on, "don't you have some kind of nickname——something for short? I am a little too drunk to say your name right . . . Give me some funny name for short. Come on!"

I had a name for her instead——Dumb Cunt——and I was about ready to terminate this Valentine Day's nightmare when she said something which would have been sort of amusing——at a different hour. "By the way, you don't have any accent and I was expecting some hard bitchy lady with a heavy accent . . . How come? Are you **sure** you're who you're supposed to be . . . Hey, Xavvviera, say something——I want to see whether it really is you. If I woke you up, I'm not sorry, because who the hell wants to sleep at night anyway! That's for the birds because you yourself wrote in your book that you only slept four hours a night."

"If I can get a word in edgewise, lady, uh, what is your name again? You've never even mentioned your name, have you?"

She answered, half-mumbling to herself, "Midge, but that doesn't matter, I am of Russian extraction, but go on, talk to me, I love your voice so far, and fuck the accent you don't have——you sound more English than Dutch anyway." All of this was said in what can only be described as a one-sentence mumble.

"Okay, I will talk to you, but only for a little bit——I really am tired," I said. "Since I am retired from my previous profession, I obviously don't have to keep such late hours anymore. Okay? Also, the last few days have been pretty hectic for me, what with my new book out, and I really can use more than four hours sleep these days. Tomorrow, for instance, I have to get up at 7:30 for a breakfast meeting with my lawyer, and since it is

226

now almost 4 A.M., I really am going to have to say goodbye to you."

She mumbled something about how hard it had been to get in touch with me, and couldn't I talk with her for just a little bit?

"All right, we'll talk for a few minutes more, and then I really must go off to sleep," I agreed. "Midge, tell me what's on your mind, and you can call me X if you need to call me something for short . . . let me guess about you. You are unmarried, in your mid-thirties, and with a slight tendency toward homosexuality. Am I right? Also, you sound too smart to be a real alcoholic, so probably something sad has happened to you to make you drink. . . ."

There was a few moments of silence on the other end, interrupted only by a soft hiccup. Then Midge said, "Hey, love, you hit the nail right on the head. My God, I'm as lonely as you can feel! I am 32, haven't too many friends, and have had affairs with both men and women."

"What do you look like?" My eternal curiosity was taking over, damn it!

"I am a little over 5'7" and right now am a little overweight. I have really big boobs, much bigger than yours . . . I know that because I saw you on television and you did look groovy so I take it back, what I said about thinking you might be bitchy. . . ."

"That's all right," I said.

"Let me tell you this about myself—two years ago I got raped—isn't that a laugh, a big girl like me getting **raped.** By golly, it was no fun . . . I might have been slightly drunk when it happened, but, Jesus, I didn't **want** it . . . I have to confess, though, that he was gorgeous, a big chocolate-colored fellow from Trinidad. I tried to kick him in the balls, but he was stronger and much bigger than me, and nothing was going to stop him. I cried a lot, and when he left I was in pain, and later black and blue from the marks he had left on me. . . ."

I said I was sorry she'd had this terrible experience.

227

"And then, would you believe it, a few weeks later I found that I was pregnant and he had been the **only** man who'd screwed me in half a year."

"That was really rotten luck," I said. God knows, I really did sympathize with her now.

"Anyway, there I was, with a fine position with a large advertising agency——one of the best jobs held by a woman in town——and a black kid in my belly. I'm not prejudiced——under different circumstances I might want to have my own kid——but not the 'love child' of a rape. Honestly, it wasn't the fact of a black kid in my tummy that bothered me so much as the fact I'd been raped. So of course I did something about it. I went to a clinic and explained the circumstances and arranged to have a so-called vacuum job abortion. This was the first time I'd been pregnant in my life, and maybe my last time. [Here there was a long painful pause.] Have you ever been pregnant, X?"

Now it was **my** turn to pause. But I decided to be as open with her as she had been with me. "Yes, when I was 19, I had an abortion——under horrible circumstances. It was in Holland. I know it's hard to believe, but I didn't get anything for pain——no injection, no anything——and I felt every bit of what was happening to me. It was all very painful, and I screamed like a pig, and the nurse stuffed big wads of cotton into my mouth to make me shut up. In those days abortion was illegal, and quite a few doctors ended up in jail.

"If you want to know, the entire experience was terrible for me——I was terribly depressed afterward, because I really had come to love what was growing inside me and hated to kill my baby. I was much further pregnant than you——three months——and things were more complicated for me, but I did realize that I was too young to have the baby, husband or no husband. Now it is a different story altogether——women have become so liberated that they are willing to have their babies and raise them on their own, and I think I have the courage to have a "love baby"——whether or not I married the father. Perhaps I would then settle in Toronto and buy

228

myself a nice condominium——of course I will have to be serious about settling down because having a child is a tremendous responsibility, particularly if there is no father in the house. It would mean giving up my trips abroad and my private life, so I honestly don't know if I'm ready for motherhood just yet. . . ."

I could hear Midge breathing on the other end, but she didn't say anything, so I said, "Listen, you didn't call me in the middle of the night to hear my plans about motherhood, so what **can** I do for you?"

"My God, Xaviera," she said with a heavy sigh, "I just want you to listen to me and maybe give me some advice. I am a mature intelligent woman, I had a terrific upbringing because my parents could afford the best for me, yet I'm so fucked up I can only look for happiness inside a liquor bottle. . . ."

At this point I was beginning to feel like one of those all-night disc jockeys who listen to people's problems and cries for help——part entertainer and part-psychiatrist. Midge didn't say anything for the next few moments, then she continued: "I think I could really dig **you,**" she said. "I know that I'm already turned on to you, and you know what got me so horny? It was that scene in your book where you carry on a long-distance conversation with Claudette and you both fantasize about each other and masturbate away while you're talking. When I read that, I just flipped out and went into the bathroom and relieved myself under the bathtub spigot, as you advised women to do in one of your **Penthouse** columns."

"Listen, Midge," I said, "I'd like to help you but I'm not going into a long-distance fantasy with you at this hour. I'm really tired and have **got** to get to bed."

"I know, I know . . . I won't keep you on much longer ——hey, by the way, talking about sexy material, when I showed your book at the office——I think I was one of the first people in town to spot the book and buy it——the guys in the office all took a look at it and they agreed that page 300 was about the horniest piece of material they'd ever read. A couple of them disappeared for a while, so what do you think **they** were doing . . . ?"

"It's the world's least expensive sport," I replied, laughing. Midge started talking again but it was getting harder to understand her because she was slurring her words worse than ever. She obviously had refilled her drink. I caught the words "girl friend," so I asked her, "Is your girl friend your lover? If so, you shouldn't be so lonely."

This seemed to sober her up some. "Hell, no," she yelled into the receiver, "she is a married chick with two kids and a bad marriage and she doesn't know whether she likes chicks or not. She also has a big mouth and I don't know if I could trust her if we had an affair——Women's Lib and all that jazz hasn't reached my office yet, and I don't know if I'd keep my job if they found out I'm gay. It's wrong and stupid, but we are still dependent on our male bosses, the fuckers!"

"Yes, I certainly agree with you there——it may be changing, but it's still very much a man's world."

"Hey, X, tell me——how can you even fall in love anymore after those years of being a prostitute? How do you separate love and sex?"

"To me, love and sex are two entirely different entities, though obviously a combination of the two is a perfect match. If I have sex with a man I love, then I love his body, his mind, his soul, everything. Love is giving before taking, sacrifice, understanding, compatibility, mutually respecting one another, vibes, passion, desire . . . but, listen, that doesn't mean that pure sex with someone you hardly know can't give you a great deal of physical pleasure. If a guy walks down the street and sees a cute girl in a miniskirt and gets turned on, that's pure horniness——he could virtually fuck her right there——and the **same** counts for me!

"The other day I did a radio interview and as I was leaving the studio, I heard a fantastic deep voice behind me. I got so turned on, without even knowing what kind of person belonged to the voice, and when I looked over my shoulder there was this gorgeous young man in his early thirties who virtually oozed virility, I walked over to him——I felt I really didn't need an introduction because everyone there must've known who I was——put my hand on his shoulder, and openly asked him, 'What are you doing for the next few hours? Let's have lunch, then go home and make love. I am **horny.** . . .'"

"My God, what did **he** do?" Midge said, sounding amazed.

"He looked absolutely shocked, then he pushed all his work to one side of the desk and we went to a cozy little restaurant for a nice lunch. Then, exactly as I said, we went back to my place and fucked all afternoon. There was no love there, but it sure was a great afternoon. And after we'd gotten into each other's bodies, we got into each other's heads. I found him a groovy fellow, smart and witty and I am sure we're going to be good friends. And hopefully I will be able to love him as a friend, though not as my one true boy friend."

Midge was quiet for a bit, then excused herself for a minute——which turned out to be more like five minutes ——and when she got back she sounded really stoned. I decided it was certainly time to end the conversation, and told her so in no uncertain terms. As if jabbed by a thousand needles, she suddenly came alive and yelled into my ear, "Don't you dare get off the phone! I need you, you are the only one I can talk to . . . don't tell me you want to get rid of me already. . . !"

I reminded her I'd been on the phone with her for well over an hour, but the only way I could get off the phone with her was to agree to have a drink with her and her girl friend when they came to Toronto to go to the tennis tournament here. I thought it very unlikely this would ever happen, but at least it allowed me to hang up and try to go to sleep.

I tried to get to sleep, all right, but not for long——the damn phone rang again in five minutes, and I picked it up, yelled "Leave me alone!" into the receiver, and slammed the phone down. I sat there, in an absolute rage, and then called the hotel switchboard and told them to hold all calls until 8 in the morning, which would only give me about three hours' sleep.

At 8 A.M. sharp the phone rang and, yes, it wasn't the hotel operator. It was Maudlin Midge, sounding apologetic as hell——and not a little hung-over——and despite my exhaustion, I did feel sorry for her. She was so lonely and mixed-up it was pathetic. But she was also relentless. I accepted her apology, saying I understood her situation, but she kept talking . . . and talking . . . and talking . . . and finally I just put the receiver down. I had a lot to do that day, and Midge, if I gave her half a chance, would have me on the phone until high noon——time, probably, for her first drink of the day.

Over the next few days I thought about Midge quite a lot. I would have liked to help her——at least talked to her under sane conditions (daylight hours, phone calls that didn't wear out my patience, not to speak of my eardrum)——but I didn't even know her last name or phone number. I couldn't remember when the tennis matches were, or even if she'd told me when they were but I promised myself that if Midge came to town and did call, I'd have to sit down and have a serious talk with her.

On Saturday, the phone rang and it was Midge and her girl friend——not only in town but actually downstairs in the hotel lobby. Bloody hell! She'd given me no warning as to precisely when she'd be in town, much less come calling on me, and here I was in the midst of a radio interview with an American journalist, who was taping an hour-long program for distribution around the U.S. I explained this to Midge, and she said this was the only time during her visit that she could see me. I told her to hold on while I discussed it with my interviewer.

His name was Freddy and he was young and blonde and kind of attractive, despite being rather shy with me. I had been having some fun teasing him, and now he really looked flabbergasted when I said, "Hey, Freddy, two women friends are downstairs——shall I have them come up? We might end up having an orgy instead of an interview——what do you say?"

"Well, uhhh," Freddy mumbled, "gee, I don't know **what** to say."

"Come on, Freddy, be a good sport." I could see he was getting turned on by the idea.

"Well, yeah, **okay**——I'm game if **you** are."

Now I had to think about Midge——was she game to get into a scene where a man was involved?

And in a moment of levity, I had to ask myself: Do other people have such problems?

I returned to the phone and said, "Midge, my interviewer has graciously consented to allow some time for you and me, but I have to warn you that if anything—— well, erotic——transpires, I would expect him to take a part. I know you may not care for the company of a man, but he's here——and my courtesy to you can be no less than my responsibility to him."

"It's okay, Xaviera," she said. "I really just want to meet you, and all this orgy talk is totally unrealistic. I mean, I don't know about me, but my friend is definitely too uptight to get into any scenes with both men and women."

What seemed like only seconds later, Midge and her friend arrived at my hotel suite. To tell the truth, I was more than pleasantly surprised to see what she looked like. She was dressed in an absolutely smashing, light-gray, pin-striped flannel pantsuit, with a soft pink blouse and matching pink scarf, and she looked very elegant. Indeed, she wore it well despite being a bit on the plump side. Her boobs were, as advertised, astonishing: of course she was wearing a bra, but they seemed wondrously large and firm, bra or no bra. As for her face, she simply had not done herself justice. Her hair, thickish and on the curly side, was worn shoulder-length and pushed behind her left ear, with a curl over the other ear. More important than her carefully constructed hair style, she really was a natural blonde and had very beautiful hair. Her eyebrows were glorious and her eyes were a brilliant bluish-green——if there's such a color——and changed as the light changed.

Her friend, Gloria, was a short slim blonde in her mid-thirties, with a Cutie Pie face. Actually it was a pretty little face, though it did remind me of the faces on dolls. And she was so petite that the two of them reminded me of Laurel and Hardy, despite their both being quite attractive women.

I introduced everyone around and made some cold drinks, and then sat down to get to know Midge better. She really was fascinating to watch. Her long, naturally curling eyelashes, tastefully accented with some light touches of brown mascara, kind of blew my mind——as did her perfect mouth, all even white teeth, and lips that could convey a lot. When Midge was talking, a semi-sarcastic grin often spread over her face, but there were clear moments of melancholy as well, and there were also instances when her lovely mouth betrayed much bitterness. If she knew she was being observed, she would make a puckish mocking face, as if to say: Don't watch me so carefully——you might learn who I really am.

Her hands also fascinated me. They were exquisite. She used them when she was making a point, and the visual movement of her slim wrists and long, yet strong, fingers was captivating. All in all, I really had to wonder why this handsome woman should lack for admirers of either sex. She had a new one, already——in me.

As the conversation progressed, Gloria and Freddy seemed to be getting along famously——they were both very interested in sports——and this left Midge and me to our mutual explorations. We sort of fenced around for a while, with Midge answering most of my questions evasively.

"Really, Midge," I said at one point, "I don't know why you should be so unhappy. You're very attractive, and if you wanted to find yourself a man, you should have no trouble."

234

"I don't know, Xaviera . . . it just never works out. I always feel insecure in a relationship with a male. It's just—well, easier, with another woman, at least for me."

"Don't **you** think you're quite attractive to men?"

"I could shed a few pounds, and it sure wouldn't hurt."

"Yes, but a quick diet would solve all that," I pointed out. "Do you ever take diet pills?"

"I have, on a few occasions, but they make me irritable and jumpy."

"I know what you mean. I once took some pills to help me go on a crash diet—I was having publicity pictures taken in a bikini—and they made me feel as though my nerves were plugged into the electric wall socket."

The mention of electricity seemed to launch Midge into another profuse apology for her telephone calls earlier in the week, but I told her to forget about it once and for all.

"No," she said. "I can't forget about it so easily. It was horribly rude of me to call you in the middle of the night. And to keep calling back—well, that's a sign of how really drunk I was."

"It's really nothing to brood about. I **was** angry with you at the time, but there was also something about you that intrigued me." As I was saying this, I was concentrating on that great face and skin—her complexion reminded me so very much of women I knew in London, their cheeks apple-like and inviting a taste—and those gigantic boobs of hers. Whatever Midge's real problems were, being sexually enticing was definitely **not** one of them.

From time to time, I paid some attention to what was going on between Gloria and Freddy, and to my small astonishment, she was acting like tennis was not precisely the game **she** had in mind. Amazingly, I later learned from Freddy that Gloria had been asking in rather explicit terms if we'd been fucking when Midge

235

called from the hotel lobby, and had it been good. At least she didn't waste time with small talk!

When Freddy reluctantly admitted that he'd not been to bed with me, Gloria began flirting with him even more openly, as though they were two teen-agers getting up the courage to have their first fuck. I thought she'd come to Toronto to watch some good tennis, but "love-all" was never far from her mind, if you ask me.

Midge and I were becoming very cozy, and I began to entertain the idea of leading us all into a cozy swing in the bedroom, or at least taking her in there with me. It never entered my mind that both women might have stopped by for a little sex-before-tennis-anyone(?). Certainly Midge had seemed too totally distressed over the phone to suspect **her** of organizing a seduction scene with her friend.

"Ah, Midge," I said, partly to test her intentions, "do you really have to make the tennis matches?"

"Oh, we so rarely get to Toronto that there are so many things I'd like to do, but Gloria, I think, really does have her heart set on making the matches. She's a real tennis buff. I like the sport, but she plays regularly—did you see how trim her figure is!—and we wrote away months ago for tickets to today's matches."

"Oh. I thought you might want to spend more time here so we could get to know each other better."

"Well, I can always come back. Winnipeg isn't two hours away by plane. I really just wanted to meet you this time, and to really apologize for the other night." Her face revealed a whole lot of emotion as she said this.

"Well," I said, deciding to take the offensive, "I am very attracted to you and you can apologize to me in the bedroom."

She looked slightly stunned at the proposal I was making, but her eyes told me that she was interested, whether or not she had the courage to go through with it. So I got up and went over to her, saying, "Who knows when we'll see each other again. Let's make the

236

most of the moment." And, meek as a little lamb, she got up from her chair and as if in a trance, took my arm as we headed for the bedroom.

"Hey, us, too!" yelled Gloria and she pulled Freddy up from the couch. They had been smooching a little there and their clothing was rumpled. My first reaction to their coming along was annoyance, but then I thought, oh, well, three's not a fucking crowd so four can be even more fucking fun. Besides, Freddy was a cute guy and I dug the idea of seeing him really make it with Gloria. So into the bedroom we all went, arm in arm, like the Four Musketeers or some loyal band of old-time friends.

Since I was clearly the Mistress of Ceremonies, I decided to play the role to the hilt, which might or might not include playing with Freddy's cock. "All right, my sex-crazed friends," I instructed them. "Let's get into it—Freddy and Gloria, you undress each other while I disrobe this delicious creature here."

Freddy and Gloria, to my surprise, began ripping the clothes off each other and in a moment she was down on her knees in front of him, her mouth hungry for cock, sucking him hard.

"Whoa there," I said, "not so fast. First you and Midge have to go into the bathroom and freshen up." Gloria looked embarrassed, like some kid with her hand caught in the cookie jar before having gotten permission even to have one cookie. She just stood there, with her pert breasts and ass sticking out, looking sheepish, while Freddy didn't seem to know what to do with his erection.

However, I was content to let them stand there, eager to get at each other, but having to watch while I luxuriously took my time undressing Midge. I undressed her piece by piece but peeled off her black bikini panties before I undid her bra, and the sight of her beautiful blonde cunt made me give it a little lick-and-a-promise before returning to the rest of her body. And the sight of her voluptuous boobs pouring out of

237

her bra also made me pay a little homage to them, taking them one by one into my mouth and sucking the nipples stiff and erect.

"Now," I said, "you and Gloria go into the bathroom and wash up a bit. If you've read my book, you know I'm a nut for cleanliness, so make yourselves . . . well, good enough to eat." Gloria giggled at this, but Midge just blushed and the two of them went into the bathroom.

While they were in there, I went over to Freddy, took his nice hard penis in my hand, and said, "Freddy, I don't think we've been introduced."

"Wh-what do you mean?"

"Who's your friend here?" I said, giving his cock a little pull.

"Wh-whoever he is, he's sure pleased to meet you," Freddy said, really feeling like a strong young stud.

Just then the two women came out of the bathroom, and I arranged the pillows on the bed so that our bodies needn't touch. Freddy, now bold as a young lion, led Gloria to their side of the big bed and lay down with her. To my surprise, they immediately went into the 69 position and were having a grand old time eating each other.

Midge seemed fascinated watching them, but I led her to our side of the bed and told her to get comfortable. Then I took care of her needs, and boy oh boy did this sex-starved lady have needs! I kissed her face and neck and shoulders and then I lavished attention on those two magnificent breasts, caressing them and gently squeezing them and licking every inch of their surface. At one point Midge was so turned on that she tried to shove an entire tit into my mouth, but it was too much flesh to contain and I almost gagged. So to control things my way, I kept taking the tips of her breasts into my mouth, sucking on the big pinkish nipples while she moaned in pleasure, and then putting my face between her breasts to kiss and lick her deep cleavage.

Midge's thighs were moving together and apart like a regular accordion and I knew I'd have to do something about that, so I moved down her body and without many preliminaries, I licked and kissed and caressed her into an orgasm that not only shook her entire body, but seemed to shake the bed as well. At least Gloria and Freddy stopped eating each other long enough to watch our love-making. Then they went right back at it, and in a minute the way Freddy's ass was acting——jerking back and forth——I could tell he was coming and Gloria, a game girl, was taking it all, every drop.

Now I could feel Midge's worshiping arms around me, enfolding me and pulling me to her, and we lay close together, with me content for the time being just to have given her all that pleasure. Finally she said, close to my ear, "Xaviera, that was really wonderful . . . that other night I should have gotten on a plane and come to see you instead of talking your ear off. You know, I was as sexed-up as I was drunk, so that after you hung up on me I took the empty whiskey bottle and used it to play with myself. But that wasn't much fun, so I took some candles and began inserting them into my pussy until there were six of them in there . . . and I moved them around in there but it was kind of uncomfortable so I took them out and went into the kitchen and found this long thin cucumber and put some vaseline on it and used it on myself. I wasn't so drunk that I didn't find this kind of degrading, but I needed to come **so** badly! As I rammed the cucumber in me, I played with my ass with my other hand and finally I did manage an orgasm, but nothing like you just gave me . . . Oh boy, look at those two go at it! I'm so glad for Gloria —she needs cock badly. . . ."

I had the feeling that Midge was going to talk as long as she had the other night, so it was a relief to watch Gloria and Freddy, who were now in the middle of a fantastic fuck. Fred was on his knees between her legs, pounding his prick into her, and she had her legs tightly wrapped around his lower back, her ass moving forward to meet his every thrust. Watching how well she fucked, I could believe she was a good tennis player!

The two of them were making all sorts of great little

animal sounds, and their commotion was turning me on. I began deeply kissing and tonguing Midge's exquisite mouth, long-lasting kisses that made her tremble with desire. Not only did she respond passionately with her tongue, it proved her mouth was useful for more than just open-ended monologues. We then moved into the 69 position but truth to tell, Midge did not do too much for me. Nonetheless, I thoroughly enjoyed myself since her cunt was absolutely delicious. She was going wild, out of her mind with lust, and her strong legs were so powerfully gripped around my neck that they kept pushing my face deeper inside her but away from her hardened clit. Finally she took my hand and gestured that I should insert a finger, or all the fingers that would fit, into her, and I put three fingers inside her and while fingering and eating her, back at the clit again, she came like an animal, screaming and shaking, and nearly giving me a broken neck in the process.

Both our bodies were wet with perspiration and when she finally relaxed, Midge pressed me in her arms and held me against her magnificent breasts, which at that moment were the nicest pillows I'd ever felt. We took a little nap this way, and so did Gloria and Freddy, and no one watched any tennis that afternoon.

When Midge and Gloria left to catch their plane back to Winnipeg, Midge promised to write—I told her, "Don't call, it's too expensive"—but she never did. I hope something worked out for her. Freddy had indicated more than a little interest in making it with Midge that horny afternoon, but she had politely, but firmly, turned him down. So I have to hope she has found herself a woman.

They're not so bad . . . women.

*   *   *

Xaviera—

Do hope this reaches you, but imagine there is little chance—nothing can be lost by trying, though. Fortunately, this correspondence couldn't possibly fall into the hands of some destitute connected with a movie production company?

Regardless, you must be swamped with psychotic mail such as this may seem to be, but please bear with this. I guess I've become infatuated with what you could be like —so—*c'est la vie.* Apparently I've been living in a bubble, for I became aware of your existence only about a month ago when a friend presented me with your book and was sure that I would enjoy it. He was right.

Maybe I'm out in left field without my glove, but I can give you more than any man and wonder if you are woman enough to enjoy it. I understand you've had a disagreement with our good ole US of A Apple Pie Government. Therefore, if you're interested, set the time and place. Please at least let me know something—

Later—

Richie Armstrong
New York, N.Y.

Dear Madam Hollander:

I know you are no longer operating your first-class brothel, but I wonder if you could do me a special favor? It would be the culmination of a lifetime wish. A delicious fantasy come to life, if you will.

I would like you to gather for me a bevy of the *most* beautiful young women you know. Only the *crème de la crème!* I want to be their tireless slave in fulfilling their sexual needs. Since I am realistic in recognizing that there are probably only "two shots," and the second one probably a mild "pop!", in my "gun" over the course of a respectably entertaining evening (four-five hours), I will have to tongue all the delicious young ladies into a state of sexual joy. I will lick and probe and suck and lap and muff-dive until everyone is totally satisfied! You may be assured that no young woman will leave the site of our glorious tryst without clitoral satisfaction—I am aware of Women's Liberation ideology, too!

You may ask yourself why "this old fart" wants to spend a lot of money on something that may at best produce an orgasm or two for him, and I will answer that giving pleasure is pleasure itself, and ego-fulfilling and, if we're lucky in the *menage* of personalities, a great deal of fun as well.

Suffice to say that I can afford my fantasies, but I desire to prove that slightly advanced age is no barrier to sexual carnivalism!

Yours, in the spirit of Eros Uninhibited,

Abe Finney

New Milford, Conn.

My Dear Xaviera,

I have read "The Happy Hooker" and enjoyed it greatly. I have taken a very special interest in you. I find you to be the most fascinating woman and not only are you intellegent, witty and well read, you are also very beautiful.

I believe that you have features that truly appeal to most people. I am in love with your eyes. They hold a mystical glow in them and it is such a turn-on, you would never believe it. I could go on forever about your mouth. It is open, sensuous and warm. I'm also turned on by your teeth, they're fantastic. I believe I am falling in love with you.

I too, like yourself, am bisexual, and I usually have men because where I live it's hard to find a nice sexy girl to be with. I'm 17 years old and I'm very mature. I've been having sex since I was 11. I have reddish brown hair, and soulful brown eyes. My shape isn't that bad, but I'm a little chubby. I'm very good in bed.

I know you're very busy, but I would really groove on

corresponding with a woman like you. I don't live far from New London.

I would really appreciate it if you wrote me. As I have said before, I am in love with you and your glorious mind.

Much love,

S. Sonja Rudnyanszky

Old Lime, Conn.

P.S. Do write soon, my Xaviera. The "S" in my first name stands for Svetlana, which I *hate!*

Dear Miss Hollander,

I just finished reading your book, "The Happy Hooker," and may I say that it was the most erotic book I have read in a long time.

Please forgive my printing but I have cerebral palsy and am in a wheelchair. I am over 21.

May I please have a sexy (nude) picture of you? And what are your measurements?

Do you know of any good prostitutes here in Boise? If so, would you please tell me how to get in touch with them since I don't know how.

Sincerely yours,

Edgar J. Wilbank

Boise, Idaho

Dear Miss Hollander,

A few months ago I read your book and enjoyed it very much. It is a book that years from now I will still be telling people about. I found it very interesting and it also gave me a completely different viewpoint on what a woman who chooses to be a prostitute can really make of herself if she sets her mind to it.

The book was written in such a way that I felt even before finishing it that I was reading about a woman I already knew personally. I enjoy reading, and have read many erotic books, but never have I received so much pleasure from one.

I have told many of my friends that you must really have a pleasing personality. I also have passed the book on to them so they also could receive the reading pleasure that I did.

I saw you on the TV program, "Panorama," and thought your interview quite interesting. One of the men on the program asked you if you didn't feel a little immature because of the ways you feel and think about sex. I felt that if he had really read your book he could have answered that question himself with a definite "no."

Now, please let me ask you a few questions that have entered my thoughts.

You stated that you are a masochist and still have marks from this form of sexual activity. Due to my inexperience of this, I fail to understand how anyone could receive pleasure from pain. To me sex is a beautiful thing and should be performed in a very gentle way. Could you please explain to me your view of this?

Also, if you enjoy sex with women how is it that you are contemplating marriage to Larry? Especially since you say you take the aggressive role when with a woman. Larry must really be a wonderful understanding person. But he also should consider himself a very lucky guy to have you for his girlfriend.

Well, Miss Hollander, I sincerely hope I haven't appeared too silly by writing to you and I do hope you can find the time to write me. I wish I could have known you before you came into the public eye. I think it would have been a pleasure to sit and talk with you on many different subjects. You appear to be a very well informed person at a very young age.

244

Please let me apologize for the length of this letter, I had a lot to say and tried to make it as brief as possible. I'll be looking for your return letter soon.

Sincerely,

Theodora Espey
Wilmington, Del.

Dear Xaviera,

I don't know if this letter will ever reach you, but I've got to try and get in touch with you some how. I've just read "The Happy Hooker," and you have got to be the most sincere and real person I've ever read about. Naturally I'd love to make it with you, but I realize how difficult it must be to get in touch with some one like you.

However, if you are still in the New York area, maybe we can work something out. I promise I'll be one of the most interesting and lovable men you've ever met. I always "love" a woman; I've never fucked anyone.

I am sure you would enjoy meeting and being with me very, very much, because you truly love and appreciate sex. Pleasing you would be a great joy to me indeed.

If you would like me to meet you, just write back and say when and where. Any Saturday except March 17th would be fine for me. I have a St. Patricks Day date already planned for that night. My best friend is playing piano in a place near home, and most of our friends are going to celebrate with him.

In fact, I'd be most flattered to bring you, but of course I wouldn't expect you to travel that far or be free (socially available).

Please let me know if you would like to meet me. I mean it when I promise you a very satisfying and extremely enjoyable evening. You can be assured of thorough psychological satisfaction. Please tell me what you think. I'll meet you anywhere, anytime, on any Saturday.

Thank you very much.

Very respectfully and with much love,

Arthur Jenkins
Jersey City, N.J.

Dear Miss Hollander:

Do you like pornography? Particularly the illustrated kind?

My boy friend and I like to lie in bed and read aloud and play with each other. It's really a turn-on—he keeps his hand in my lap and just kids around and I give his cock and balls a gentle going-over and when we're ready —when we can't stand it any longer—we try out one of the positions in the book.

It keeps life interesting and it's certainly a lot more fun than watching TV.

One of the couples we hang out with thinks it's "artificial stimulation," and they don't approve. I say that anything that helps keep your sex life active and different is a good thing. What do you think?

Sincerely,

Bess Greenfield
Woodstock, N.Y.

Dear Miss Hollander,

Just a short note to tell you how great we thought your first two books have been and how much my wife and I are looking forward to your third book.

It is pleasing for us to see someone put their foot forward to express themselves and their feelings openly.

Through reading your books, we find you live in a world of restaurants and take out food services and it's because of this we would like to offer our hospitality to you and your boyfriend. We are not part of the swinging scene, but rather feel a day off for you, from your hectic schedule, would be appreciated and of course very interesting and fascinating for us.

Our invitation is very sincere and if you haven't had a good home-cooked meal for sometime it may be a rather nice change.

We are a young couple, myself being 23 and my wife 19. We have been married for 9 months.

I'm sure you received a great many invitations but we thought that we'd drop you this line in hope that you'd be interested. We promise you a quiet, relaxing day, something which you might not be familiar with but would greatly appreciate.

Also we are quite upset we couldn't be at Burlington Mall but due to previous commitments were unable to make it.

Please acknowledge our letter by dropping us a line saying whether or not you would be interested in coming to see us, at a date convenient to you (Saturday or Sunday preffered if possible). We know you won't regret it.

Sincerely,

John & Elspeth Brothers
Kitchener, Ontario

Dear X-y Lady,

I read your book and I was very impressed with your life-style.

My main interest lies in giving service to women who are bored and frustrated with their daily existences.

I want to go into the stud business—which would include women, couples and men, since I can swing both ways. My credentials are: Black, 6'1", 185, manly, charming, sensitive, magnetic, shaved head, and, most of all, very charismatic.

I would appreciate a response from you, Xaviera, since I think we'd dig each other's personalities and life-styles.

Your friend, I hope,

Christopher James Logan III
Newark, N.J.

Dear Miss Hollander:

As a representative of the great French nation, I deeply resent your statement that Frenchmen are good pussy-eaters, but do not themselves smell hygienically proper.

I can offer, as a clear statement of fact, my claim that I have personally "eaten" at least 150 Frenchwomen and have never once been assaulted by any of the barbaric experiences to which you so cruelly allude. My tongue has moved from pussy to grand cuisine without a moment's hesitation. All dishes were to the gourmet born!

Vive la France!

Michel Peri
Grenoble, France

Dear Miss Hollander:

I am writing to you post haste lest I lose the courage to do so.

Your book forced a lot of secret yearnings in me to escape the nice comfortable dungeon I placed them in, and forced me to ask myself what I want from life. I'm not sure, but one answer is obvious enough: more sex!

I suppose that I'm still young enough and idealistic

enough to believe that a famous person such as you now are is really interested in her readers and admirers—I hope you don't disappoint me! I'm anxiously waiting to hear from you—with "baited breath," as they say, in bad—God, were there any other kind?—Victorian novels.

Please do write. I have so much I want to ask you.

Yours most sincerely,

Claire-Sabrina McGhee
Memphis, Tenn.

Dear Miss Xaviera,

I have just finished your incredible book and you sound simply fantastic and gorgeous.

I know I do not have any right to write to you. I am a man of modest means and a modest income and I know you have probably had letters from others that have much more than I. I want very much to make love to you. No, I don't think I am that good a lover but I believe in trying to satisfy a woman completely. How wonderful it would be to do that with you and I dream I could satisfy you.

I live in an apartment just outside of Washington, D.C. Would there be any way possible to have you here, but you probably will howl with laughter and throw my letter away.

I am 37, 5 feet 10 inches tall and weigh 150 pounds. I am what you'd call wiry.

Just in case you call, my phone is listed.

I haven't much, just a plain guy who wants to make love with you.

Thank you.

Sincerely,

Max Pollett
Washington, D.C.

249

Dear Xaviera,

I just finished your book a few weeks ago and I must tell you that it was very convincing to me as regards the need to legalize prostitution. I have always felt this way. But your words gave me far greater insight into what a great service they perform in a community.

I have recommended your book to many friends and loaned my own copy to several others. Finally I went out and bought a half dozen more copies to give to friends. Sometimes I think it's all we talk about.

I have been seriously debating about whether or not to organize a Madam Xaviera Hollander Fan Club. It would serve the useful purpose of learning how many people are really for legal prostitution and want to help get it launched.

What do you think about this? Do you think it's a good idea? I would appreciate it if you would write and give me your opinion and if you would go along with it. If you don't like the idea, I will certainly respect your wishes and not go ahead with it. It's only an idea in the infant stage. I haven't worked out the bugs, yet.

We might call it a fan club rated XXX for adults only.

No, I'm kidding about that.

Do let us hear from you and good luck in whatever you're doing.

Most sincerely,

Mrs. Clyde (Thelma) Kingman

Des Moines, Iowa.

Dear Xaviera,

I'm a well-endowed Filipino male of 33 who happens to have the unusual avocation of collecting panty hose.

Since you are a lovely vivacious woman who most probably puts her panty hose to full and unusual use, would it be too much to ask you for an old pair of yours in ex-

250

change for a new pair from me? I would really like to add yours to my collection.

I will be checking my P. O. Box, starting next week, hoping to hear from you and learning that you are agreeable to my request. And please don't bother washing them before you send them.

In anticipation,

Tomas C. O. Fallo
Honolulu, Hawaii

My Dear Ms Hollander:

I enjoyed reading "The Happy Hooker," and would suggest that you retitle it. In the first place, by your own account, you were not all that "happy". You may not have been "happy" most of the time, but you certainly were "horny". In the second place, most people do not know the meaning of the word "hooker". In certain urban areas and among some sophisticates, this word has the proper connotation. When you leave these circumscribed areas, the word "hooker" has no meaning whatsoever. It is a word not used by the average person. As a consequence, the sale of your excellent book is greatly restricted. However, most people know the meaning of the word "horny". If you changed the title of your book to "The Horny Hooker," it would surely increase sales tremendously. Think about it and act accordingly.

In your book, you did a great piece of autobiographical reportage. You come out as a basically good person with delicate sensibilities and a love for the intellectual life, as well as the physical. You are now a teacher, lecturer and writer, instead of a high class madam and prostitute. The point I wish to make is, that you are limiting your capabilities. Why not establish a school of higher education in The Arts of Love? You now have enough prestige to go forward with a project of this magnitude. In our developing culture, this school would be a great advancement and a civilizing influence. Schools like this existed in other enlightened eras.

A good name for this school would be THE UNIVERSITY OF VENUS AND APOLLO. It would be no problem at all to arrange for a charter, a proper endowment and accreditation. People like Masters and Johnson, Dr. Ginsberg, Dr. Rubin and many others, would be proud to have professorial status at this great university. There would be courses in Anatomy, so that all of the tactile areas sensitive to titilation or excitation could be pinpointed and so noted. Courses in Sexual Intercourse, in it's many variations, including all the positions depicted by the great statues and frescoes of India, would be required of all students. Books by Havelock Ellis and Kraft-Ebbing would be required reading in the study of the sex habits of primitive man and the aborogines. We need to learn how it all started and how it grew. Studying the past can be helpful to bring about a better sex life for this generation and those who come after.

There were great periods in history when sexual freedom was permitted and encouraged. Then came the dark ages, when organized religion obliterated all freedoms. We are now in a new age of freedom and we should take full advantage of it. This great university would be the next logical forward step that is indicated, to continue the pursuit of happiness that our constitution guarantees to all of us. We must not drop the ball now.

THE UNIVERSITY OF VENUS AND APOLLO would draw students from all over the world, since courses in many related subjects would be available. Art, Literature, Theatre Arts, Poetry Reading, Exotic Dancing, Belly Dancing, Music, Personal Hygiene, Venereal Diseases, Cunnilingus, Partner Consideration and even Thought Wave Transmission to bring partners together for love making, would be on the curriculum. For the men, there would be special courses in Cocksmanship. For the women, a course in the control of the vaginal musculature, as the women in the Near East practice it, so that any degree of constriction can be applied to the penis during sexual intercourse.

The students would be housed in co-ed dormitories on campus, in order to help each other with their homework.

At the conclusion of the prescribed studies, students would receive degrees in "Bachelor in the Arts of Love" or B. A. L. Graduate work could be continued to earn a Masters degree or even a Doctorate. As a matter of fact, a Doctorate Degree would be in order for you at this time, if this university were in existence, since you have written a worthy thesis, even though you mistitled it. In order not to deprive you of this proper recognition, I am taking it upon myself to issue to you this well deserved Doctorate Degree, so that you can be recognized as a woman of letters, instead of a scarlet woman.

You have my very best wishes for a successful career in your expanding enterprise. Please let me hear from you if I can be of any service with THE UNIVERSITY OF VENUS AND APOLLO.

Most sincerely,

Jacques Schmidt
Aspen, Colo.

THE UNIVERSALITY OF MAN

KNOW ALL MEN AND WOMEN BY THESE PRESENTS THAT

XAVIERA HOLLANDER

Has proved by her thesis that she has Professorial Status in

Fucking Methodology, Greekology, Anilingusy, Cunnilingus, Swingology,

Fuckology of the Testes, Fellatio, Dildoism, Sadism, Masochism, Orgiology

and all other requisite subjects in The Art of Love.

By the authority granted to me as an academician of high note and a man

of many letters (and postcards), I hereby confer on you the degree

Doctor of Fuckology

and grant you all of the Rights, Privileges and Honors thereto pertaining.

Given this date August 19-1972 *Witness my hand*

Dear Xaviera (Xaviera like in Riviera, but with a "zah" sound in front),

I have never written to a celebrity, author, prostitute, nymphomaniac, girl from Holland, or a Jewess cocksucker, cuntlapper, and etc. But right now I am writing to a compassionate humanitarian.

I've read both of your books. From these books you show yourself to be an exceptional kind of person.

I am not talking about your sexuality. I think 95% of humanity has the ability to suck, fuck, blow and lick various parts of the anatomy. These are basic sexual instincts we are born with, I believe. You have developed your physical sensuality to an extremely high level of attainment. For this I hardly commend you.

However, you have developed a part of your anatomy which is the hardest of all—it distinguishes man from animal. I am talking about your head, of course. Not that many people have it together enough to lay bare their lives in ink and set it in 739 pages and have it duplicated several million times for the world to read.

Always during your life you have found time to open up your heart, head, body, and even (on a more crude level) your pocket book. Compassion is a human but self-developed attribute, whereas passion, while it is an attribute, is not—dogs, chickens, elephants have passion.

In all you do, I wish you love.

Dave Regan

Juneau, Alaska

Dear Ms. Hollander:

I trust this letter will find you in good health.

In reading your new book, I noticed that you are now ensconced in Toronto, Canada. It's a very nice city.

I am most enchanted with you as a woman, and would feel privileged to share a boudoir with you if only for a few moments.

I suspect I will be in Toronto, for matters of business, before very long. If you are still feeling altruistic and genuinely concerned for the welfare of mankind, please reply with your phone number so that we may get together for a few humanistic moments.

Suffice to say that I am truly interested in your technique of horizontal analysis, and would be forever indebted to you. I suspect my wife would not be overjoyed at this overture of mine to you, but even Adam had to taste the forbidden fruit. What Earth's first man dared, dare I do less?

Adoringly,

Herman Fischoff
Concord, New Hamp.

Dear Miss Hollander,

I am a three-year-old pedigreed airdale, registered with the American Kennel Club. Your book really turned me on (my mistress read it to me). I especially liked the part about how you turned on another dog. Was he an airdale? Could I have his address?

If you get to Vermont, I hope we can romp together.

Ardently,

Clarence
Killington, Vt.

P.S. Yeah, this is a gag letter. Arf arf.
— The guys in Hartford Hall at the University of Connecticut

256

Dear Xaviera,

I'm in the process of reading your second book after having read your first one a while back. I've been wanting to write to you for awhile but I didn't think you'd ever get it but it's worth a try. You're really an interesting woman from what I read and I'd really like to meet you and really sit down and rap to you—so much of the way you think I agree with. I've had some of the same kind of experiences you've had yet you've had some that really interest me. You just really have done lots of things I'd like to do, and you are really someone I hope to meet.

I'm 21 years old, but in some ways an old 21. I've been a hooker but I can't say I've made it to the top like you did, but I've had some weird experiences with Johns similar to some you've had. But like you, I am not really doing it any more. My name is Jan, I'm 5'4", 115 lbs., blondish hair and blue-green eyes. I live with a man named Earl. We're very different but it kind of reminds me of the way you described Larry in your second book. Earl knows I want to meet you. I'm sure he'd like to also.

Well I just wanted to write and let you know how I feel about you. You really have a good, well liberated head and I know very few people whom I can relate to on such an open level. I think I could talk to you about lots of things that we'd really both dig.

Well I've gotta go now, the gas man is here and I want to fuck him, so write back if this ever gets to you *ok?*

Bye.

Jan Carlyle

Columbia, S.C.

Dear Xaviera:

I truly liked your book "The Happy Hooker."

What is your opinion on legalized prostitution? The Bar Association in California voted in favor of legalized prostitution at their last conference.

I imagine the people of California will have a chance to

vote on it within the next few years and I really do believe it will pass. Then you could set up franchises of H.H.H. (Happy Hooker Houses).

With all of the pay-offs out of it, the prices would be more reasonable and more profit to you and the girls. Think about it. I'm interested in your opinion.

Visit beautiful California sometime.

Sincerely,

J. Hughes Rice, Chairman

Rice Enterprises

Berkeley, Calif.

Dear Miss Xaviera,

I am a 17-year-old woman who would like to be a prostitute. I have always thought I wanted to be a prostitute but, until I read your book, I didn't know how right I was. I loved every page of your book about your dynamite life —how I would have loved to share that life with you! Every loving minute of it!

Every true woman should be proud of her body, as you are of yours—and I am of mine. I would love it if you could teach me all about how to be a good prostitute.

I hope you don't think I'm kooky or spaced out, writing you like this, but I have always been outspoken and said whatever came to my head. I think you must be the same way yourself.

I hope you wrote other books because I'm dying to read them all. I showed your book to my probation officer and he read it and thought it was outasight.

You wrote in your book about helping out girls who have the potential to become successful madams. I think I have that leadership quality you mentioned—all I need is a good leader. If I had worked for you—that would have been fantastic—I think you'd have seen it for yourself.

Please write back because I'm dying to hear from you, and maybe even meet you some day.

Love you sincerely,

Zita Reich

Tulsa, Okla.

Dear Miss Hollander,

I really don't know how to start this but here goes! I'm now reading your second book and must say am enjoying it emencely. I can't wait until I finish to write to you.

I'm a 22 year old house wife with a wonderful 26 year old husband and also a 7 month old son who we just adore. We are the usual middle class type couple struggling to make a living. We love each other and we love sex in every single way. We both have our freedom to have other lovers any time we want as long as we are frank with each other and if possible try to do our flinging together. One thing we hate is sneaking around about sex. I feel it should be straight forward and on the line.

Now to our problem. We never seem to find the right people to share sex with. We have one couple who are very friendly with us and we've done a little fooling around. Mostly with the man and me. His wife, although she says she loves sex all the way, never seems to get involved. I seduced her once and I really had a ball. She's beautiful and very slim which I envy. She seemed to really enjoy it. But never tried to start anything again. I value her friendship too much to be pushy. Her husband is a great lover and she doesn't mind sharing him with me at all. He has a really beautiful cock which I could suck forever. He's much bigger than my husband. I sometimes wonder if my husband isn't jealous.

Anyway, this couple is the only people we know that we can even get near to. Also the only other people I've ever gone to bed with other than Hank of course. We've made love with other couples but no sharing went on. Hank made it once with my girlfriend but he said she was a lousy lay and he didn't even enjoy it. So to boil it down, where in hell does a nice couple find some people to make it with that won't think we're absolutely mad? Which is the usual responce. We just want to ball, but we want to feel something for the people. Their is always an excuse for not making it with so and so. "If only you lived next door. I'd love to make it with you. I know we could have a real ball." Blah Blah.

I love the agressive role with a man or a woman.

Well this is certainly a confusing mess for you. But really, if you ever do get this I really would love some ideas on how to find some prospective "friends" for us. If ever you have the time to, drop me a line. And of course if your ever in Roanoke look us up.

Sincerely Ment,

Alicia Daley

Roanoke, Va.

Dear Xaviera,

Hoping that this letter will reach you, I have a very emotional hangup.

I am twenty years old and have been going out with my boyfriend for three and a half years. He was the first and only boy who has ever made love to me. I really love him and I hope he loves me just as much. My problem is that I have never reached an orgasm. I enjoy sex but not as much as I definitely should.

I feel that because sex is a great part in our lives, I try to be as receptive as possible. I do not feel loose. I still feel some inhabitions about sex.

Occasionally, when we have to "rush" our love making, I can understand how I wouldn't be able to get an orgasm.

260

But for six months we were living together in an apartment, and even then, it didn't help. Do you think that you could give me some advice, as I have just finished your second book, I have, Xaviera. I found it so interesting I called in to work to say I was sick just to finish reading it.

One thing I just wanted to comment on was that I felt very sorry about your getting stiffed by that phony producer "Irving Rubeen." Somehow, from the beginning of that chapter I felt he was a fake. Oh well, just a little comment of mine.

I really hope you will be able to answer my letter personally as I have been very upset about this.

I realize, with your third book and such that you are a very busy woman, but if it would be possible to just jot down some of your advice, I would dearly appreciate it.

Yours truly,

Michele Nicholson
Sault-Ste.-Marie, Ontario

Dear Miss Hollander:
I am the editor-in-chief of a high school journal called *Spectrum*. The journal's purpose is to make students more aware of the world they live in by having different personalities write articles for us. The editorial staff has decided to have an article in one of our future issues about prostitution. Most of us on the staff have either read your book or have seen you on television at one time or another and we unanimously decided to ask you to write the article for us.

When you are through writing the article, please send it as soon as possible to this address:

Spectrum

[no address included]

261

Thank you very, very much for your help and your cooperation.

Yours truly,

Jeffrey Ressner

P.S. We are an underground journal so you do not have to worry about censorship.

Dear Miss Hollander,
I read the London *Evening Standard* and I take a very dim view of the things you said about Englishmen being lousy lovers, got no life in them, and absolutely sexless, so let me tell you that you have not yet met a real Englishman. The kind you meet around your circles of life are nothing but pimps, narks and throwouts, and you estimate them all as typical of Englishmen. How wrong you are. I can say the same thing about your class of society tarts, like you, put your hand on their breast and they scream the place down. Have a stroll around the poorer parts of London and you'll get all you want, in fact more than you can take. If I find a tart who wants love, I can dish it out, as I've had West End pros who even gave me my money back and even wanted me to live with them, and I did twice, but they wanted the West End gay life. But I satisfied them in every way, and they loved it, and I'm sure I could make any woman BEG for more, so if you fancy your luck, with a full night of love, here's your chance. I am only a poor old working Londoner, but I've got my talents, and would love to have a night with you, so if you're not "milky", try it. I won't give my address or phone number, but if you're interested in a night that could be different, and an experience for you, place an Advert in *Daily Mirror* Personals Column, thus: "Xaviera agrees,"

also a number to phone, and I will call you and arrange something, so how about it, Sexy!

Here's Hoping,

Alfie Pryce-Jones
London, England

Dear Mlle. Hollander:

I have almost finished reading your most interesting book, "The Happy Hooker."

It is interesting not merely because of the subject matter, sexual activity, but also because it shows the mentality of the American perhaps as well as any other book now extant. (A mentality I deplore.)

I have many comments and observations I could make on your experiences and the significances that lie behind them, and I wish it were possible for you and I to correspond, if you have the time or inclination. Let me assure you beforehand that I am not a potential customer, because when it comes to my own sexual activity my heart and mind and feelings are always involved, and my attitude is totally different from that of the American male. My mind is essentially that of a Hindu yogi, embracing the Vedantic philosophy, and related to a mystical frame of relevance, although I am not religious.

The human body can be made to enjoy itself through sexual contact with another, as you know; it can also be made to enjoy itself on a plane of sensitivity far beyond the dreams of anyone who merely feels sexual satisfaction, through yoga. I can tell you all about that if it interests you.

I speak French and Spanish moderately well, and Japanese and Tahitian a little. I love people in general in spite of their shortcomings. I love classical music and I have 4,000 songs at home I can play, including 1,600 Japanese songs. To me, art and talent in people make them superior, not money or education or good looks.

I am not implying anything, just making conversation, when I say I can make love to a woman all night long without seeking or thinking of my own sexual satisfaction, if it is a woman I care about, and much of this is only gentle stroking and caressing and soft words. For to me making love is not something to hurry through and seek orgasm as the goal and the end; but it is the process itself that is beautiful when done with deep feelings for the other person, relaxing them and making them feel secure.

That will suffice for now. *Veuillez-vous m'ecrire quelques mots? Si pudiera Ud. me escribir un poquito, eso me gustaria mucho! Ara'ua'e* ("later," in Tahitian).

Michel Josephson
Mexico City, Mexico

Dear Xaviera Baby!
I have read all the best sections of your wild book. I have found them pretty damn educational. I am 16 years old and I love sex, but I am in an all-boys school so I have to wait until I get home. But the girls at home are all amatures. I would like to visit your establishment, but I am broke—for the foreseeable future.

I am 5 foot nine inches and, without being too immodest, I am very well hung.

Next week I start a two-and-a-half-weeks' vacation, and I would, frankly, like some sex. If you can send me a letter indicating your location in this period, and make a reasonable price, because, remember, I'm only sixteen-years-old! In any case, I am going to need some sex pretty soon, believe you me! I will come to New York to have some sex

264

with you at your apartment, on a strictly friendship basis, late next week. Okay?

P.S. I AM A HORNY SON OF A BITCH.

Lustily yours,

Dom Luciano
Providence, R.I.

Dear Miss Hollander:
I thought you might like to hear the reaction to your two books by a 45-year-old "square" who teaches elementary school children.

1. I wish *all* my students (and all the world, for that matter) had your honesty!

2. I feel you are just as much of a prodigy in the field of eroticism and sexuality as were such people as Mozart, Goethe and Freud in their respective fields.

3. Although your second book had many more rough spots (in terms of style) than the first, there is one section that is likely to become landmark reading in the field of erotic literature. I'm referring to the passage beginning in the center of page 28 with the words "We decided to take a shower together," and ending at the top of page 31 with the phrase, ". . . and his arms around mine."

In my opinion, if all the sexually troubled people in the world were to throw out their marriage manuals and other "how-to" guides and commit this passage to memory, they'd surely be well on their way to a blissful recovery.

You are probably at least ten years ahead of your time, Miss Hollander. Your leaving is just as surely a loss to the country as was the expulsion of Charlie Chaplin many years ago. He, too, was ahead of his time.

I trust that in years to come we will come to our senses and welcome you back with the same enthusiasm we did

Chaplin on his recent triumphant return. As one Jew to
another, let me end by saying: *zeit gezunt und stark!*

Sincerely,

Jacob Fanning
Bridgeport, Conn.

Dearest Xaviera,

I just finished reading both of your remarkable books
and I've enjoyed every word written.

If I were able to choose anyone in the world to personally meet and get to know, that person would be you. I believe you'd be the only woman in the entire world that
could outcharm a Queen, stand above all actresses and
be "The Lady of all Ladies." To you I give my upmost
respect and admiration.

Your books have touched me emotionally and I feel as
if I know you myself like you probably have made thousands of others feel.

I've found a little town on Prince Edward Island called
Summerside. A very friendly place and very real people.
I've also found a real guy that I'm going to center my life
around. Within a year I hope to have children. If a boy,
will be named after Henry. And if a girl, to my respect and
devotion even though we've never met, Xaviera Christine.
I hope you won't mind.

Xaviera, if your ever on Prince Edward Island, or wish
to visit, drop in anytime. I think Summerside would be a
fine place to go for relaxsation. If you wish to bring Larry
or any other companion, your both very much welcomed
in our home.

This place is like going back fifty-sixty years in time,
but we do have modern convientciens.

Thank you for giving me hours of enjoyment by your

book. Good luck and take care of yourself alright? God
Bless You.

Sincerely,

(Mrs.) Ruth Georgene Gleason

Summerside

Prince Edward Island

Dear Ms. Hollander:
I've read your book, and while I found it vastly entertaining, I don't believe a word of it—not for a minute. The
whole bloody mess *has* to be pure, unmitigated fiction—
and bad fiction at that. I might have taken at face value
your account of your sexual proclivities—though God
knows some of your exploits beggar belief—but your in-
credibly dreary choice of men with whom to fall in love
reads like a warmed-over confession story by a dissolute
writer completely drained of imagination.
No woman allegedly as sophisticated as you claim to be
in your quasi-public affairs could be that bloody indiscreet
in her truly private life!
This may seem entirely pedantic to you, but I like to
separate my fiction from my non-fiction.
Yours in the cause of accuracy,

Morton W. Tenzer

Washington, D. C.

Dear Mlle. Hollander:
Naturally the cranks and scolds of polite society will
chide you for defying their bluenose traditions, but the
progress of mankind was ever thus!

Honi soi qui mal y pense!

Congratulations on your lance thrust into the soft underbelly of sham and Puritan hypocrisy!

Countess Nina von Rittenstein

Palm Springs, Calif.

Dear Miss Hollander:

I guess this comes under the 'Now It Can Be Told' Department.

In my usual humdrum life, it's open the cab door or open the apartment door, say hello, say Good morning and Good afternoon, and hope for good tips at Christmas.

But opening the cab door for you or for one of your "girls," with those little glimpses of thighs and breasts, well, you can't imagine how you gals helped brighten my day.

I guess you'd have to say I built my whole secret fantasy life around you kids, and now it's back to getting my kicks from listening to the ball game.

What I want to say is—and I'm sure I speak for all the other doormen guys in the old block—I sure miss the excitement of those days. So come back as soon as you can.

—Your doorman

Dear Miss Hollander,

I was very intrigued by "The Happy Hooker." You are a true Sybarite. I admire you for being able to get what you want, when you want it, and where.

My own problem involves a man (age 35) who I am fascinated by. I'm 18 myself. I've been pursuing him for almost four years. He's been away at school 400 miles away so we haven't had much time together. I really want to have sex with him (as he is the *only* male I've ever desired). This is very important. The thought of even trying to get interested in someone else is depressing. Now he's only 15 miles away and it would be very easy to see each other very often.

The only thing I want from him is sex. And lots of it. Should I proposition him with "I want to ask you something—won't you take me to bed with you?"

Does that sound okay, or is it too brazen? Please accept this as a very serious letter! When he walks into the room I get wet, you know where.

With much gratitude,

Cynthia Myers
Eastern Michigan University
Ypsilanti, Mich.

Dear Xaviera,

If you can cast your mind back to the second impossibly hot week in August, you'll recall that you motored from San Remo, Italy to St. Tropez, France. En route you picked up two of my mates hitching, a Swiss guy and an Argentinian, whom you knew more intimately. You lent Marcello "The Happy Hooker," and after meeting you for a short spell on "La Plage Tahiti" was wondering (hopefully) if I bought and re-read the book again would you sign it for me—recalling experiences of St. Tropez? Don't think me brash, but it would really mean a lot to me. OK? Hoping to recieve a reply. With remembrances of a past never to be shared again.

Yours gratefully,

Anthony Vance
Kingston, Ontario

Dear Miss Hollander,

I am taking a few minutes off from my studies to write you this letter.

I am 40 years old and went back to college last year as a freshman. For many years I went through life with the idea that I was not very smart, as I dropped out of college when I was 18. After seeing a psychologist, I decided to go back and try again.

All that I can tell you is that after reading your book, you seem to be on the same level of thought as me. You tell it like it is. I try to live my life like that and sometimes run into trouble.

To make a long letter short, I would like to talk to you whenever you get to Toronto again. I will gladly drive up there and if you allow me, talk and maybe have some dinner.

That's all, dinner. No sex. My sex life is fine—have you been on a college campus lately! And thank God they dig older men. The combination of my experience and their delicious horniness is making my college education a very joyous thing.

Hope we meet, because I may have some good stories for you,

John J. Kranis
Cleveland, Ohio

Dear Miss Hollander,

I know that you probably receive all types of mail, but I'm also confident you can spot the ones that are really sincere.

First, the book. I read it twice and it's really out of this world. Most of the things mentioned there I've also done myself. But although I've wanted to establish a similar kind of service in Mobile, I guess I'm too soft-hearted at times. I find myself giving it away for free when I should be charging.

I'm 31, but I look a lot younger. I can pass for being in my early 20s. I started out as a masseuse in Los Angeles and really dug my work. Then I worked as a stewardess for a chartered airline, where the policy was coffee, tea or me. And it was usually me. I don't think there's any part of a plane I haven't been laid in or given head in.

But all the while I've really had the "Happy Hooker" mentality—I wanted to run a house of my own. I made a lot of money as a masseuse and as a free-lance airline hustler and I now have the money to go into business on my own. But I need some guidance by an expert like you before I start lining up girls.

Please let me know if you are interested in giving me some pointers on how to stand Alabama on its ear. I could fly to see you wherever you happen to be.

Hoping very sincerely to hear from you.

Joyce Carr

Mobile, Ala.

Dear Madam Hollander:

May the wrath of God descend upon your heretic head for the evils your body has cast upon Mankind!

May your womanly parts shrivel and dry up!

May your sexual pleasure become torment!

May your soft arms cry out for a man in the night and there be none there!

And may God have mercy on your soul!

One of His Swords,

Mrs. Rosalie Dressner

Brownsville, Texas

Dear Miss Hollander,

I am a 25-year-old guy and *very* sexually-oriented.

A friend lent me a copy of your book and I couldn't put it down. O wow!

I now have a more informed and healthier attitude toward love-making. I really want to extend my admiration for the frankness and regard it must have taken for you to have written this book. I really don't think any American girl could have done it.

I hope that prostitution becomes legalized in our lifetime. As a sociologist, I feel it has a legitamite purpose and role in society when and if that society is perceptive enough to know itself and what relativity a concept like morality has.

On a more personal basis, I hope that some day (when you feel you're ready) you fall in love "once and for all," as they used to say in fairy tales, and have a truly healthy life.

I may be a scientist, but love is where it's at.

Sincerely,

Warren Pymes
Springfield, Ohio

Dear Xaviera:

Believe me—I'm not trying to get on your good side when I say that your book meant more pleasure for me than any in memory. Years ago I really got heated up by "Forever Amber," and more recently I got more than my money's worth from Harold Robbins, but you beat them all by a wide margin—and not fiction, either!

I'm sure that the movie companies must be beating at your door for the movie rights to your story. I can't wait to see the movie when it comes out.

Being of the male sex, I love a beautiful woman. So I just have to ask—do you have long hair?

A last question—do call girls like you have time to carry on a correspondence with a person who admires them. I've known quite a few girls in Reno, but I could never get them to write.

I remain

Michael Willoway
Sante Fe, New Mexico

Dear Madame,
Since I just finished "The Happy Hooker" (liked it real well!), I thought maybe you could help me with my problem.

I am 23 years old and my husband is in the army in Germany, therefore I am alone quite a lot. For St. Valentine's Day I received a pair of Ba Wa balls as a gift (or a gag). To my dismay, there were no directions for using them. They fit you-know-where, but I don't know how to use them. Are they for real and do they really work?

I realize you must be receiving a lot of letters as a result of the book, but your the only authority I can trust.

Thank you,

Mrs. Amy K. Hillquist
Bismarck, N. Dakota

Hi X:
I'm writing this letter today, because, I didn't get around to writing it yesterday or the week or month or year before. I'd really been dying to write you for the longest time since I read "The Happy Hooker." But as they say *"Morgen, morgen nur nicht heuter,"* (which is about the extent of my Deutsch by the way). Anyhow, I've

been reading "Xaviera!" recently, and that re-motivated me.

Funny, but since I put pen to paper I can't come up with any profound statements.

Last year when I first picked up "The Happy Hooker," I did so only because of curiosity. Your picture and the fact that it was to be a no bullshit thing. I guess I wanted to read it to see if I could accept it. Anyway, it was a neat book. I enjoyed it and later I found out from my brother-in-law that you were real. I took his word as fact because he's some kind of nose-picker for N.Y. State.

I really didn't want to make with the life history so I'll cut short. So in case this doesn't get to you X, don't send me a rubber stamped anything. But if it goes all the way (pun) I just want you to know if you make it to Pensacola you're always Welcome to fall in.

Sanford I. Jorgensen

Pensacola, Fla.

P.S. if you've got time to drop me a line fine, if yuh can't, be good, if not be careful, if not name it after me.

love, much xx's & Sex,

Sandy

Dear Xaviera,

I loved your book, but I didn't find anybody like me in it.

My main hangups are great legs and masturbation. I especially dig a woman wearing black stockings and I love to look at a woman when she doesn't know I'm watching and jack-off. I actually prefer it over intercourse.

My first experience was on a bus trip where an extremely beautiful woman was sitting across from me, asleep with her dress raised thigh-high. It got me so aroused that I

274

couldn't help looking at her and masturbating. I really enjoyed it and for the last eight years that's how I've been getting my kicks. I have been caught in the act many times but only received one complaint and that was also on a bus trip. The woman said, "If you want to get off, I'd appreciate it if you would go to the bath room." It embarrassed me so much that I immediately changed my seat.

Are there any more around like me or should I see a pshycharitrist? I'm 28 years old but masturbate like a 14 year old.

"Jack Happy"

Leonard Farrow

Murfreesboro, Tenn.

Dear Miss Hollander,

Hi! My name is James Donegan. I have a favor to ask of you, and I thought perhaps you'd understand.

First, I have only been to New York City once in the twenty years of my life. I don't know anyone there. I had planned on trying to live in New York City because I thought it would be the best place for me to get into the acting field.

I went to New York recently but it was a disaster and I left the same day. Not even Traveler's Aid could help me.

I have family, but don't bother with them. I'm trying to make it on my own.

Plus, I have another problem. I am a "transexual." If you aren't familiar with the term, which I can't believe, I have the physical characteristics of one sex and the mental makeup of the other sex. In my case, I want to be a woman. It is possible to change sex through hormone treatments, electrolisis of unnescesary hair, and finally the sex reassignment operation itself.

Anyway, Miss Hollander, the favor I wanted to ask was, if I came to New York again, would you allow me to stay in your apartment temporarily until I get to know people and can get established?

Besides, I'd really like to meet you and be friends. I'd truly appreciate your help. And, you could use me in your next book. It would be something new—so and so, the transexual you met. . . .

Please think it over and let me know. I'm sorry if I've been too abrupt or said anything out of the question. I hope I hear from you soon and you'll at least let me visit you.

With sincere admiration,

James Donegan
New Bedford, Mass.

Dear Xaviera,

This letter may seem a bit awkward and unusual from your regular mail but please bear with me for a moment or two and you'll understand my reason for writing.

I have read both of your books and they are both *SUPER GREAT!* Your complete honesty is a quality to be admired. Most of us never come to the place in life where we can be so honest with ourselves about what we really like. I have never in my whole life been so turned on physically, emotionally and mentally as I was when reading your books.

I feel as though I knew you and then on the other hand, I feel as though you are someone I desperately need to know. I know that you don't, under normal circumstances, answer letters privately, but would you please make an exception just this once? You'll never know just how happy you could make me.

Of course the ultimate dream would be to meet you someday. Do you have plans for being in Chicago or St. Louis soon? Any chance for a meeting?

I can assure you that I am not some sort of a jackass.

It's just that somehow you seem to be a part of my life and it seems very important to me to make it a reality. After all, you don't know just whether you would enjoy knowing me or not, do you? Why not find out?

Drop me a line and I can assure you that you will have made one person *very* happy. Until then, wherever you are, remember that someone is thinking of you always.

Yours,

Andrea Bergman

Peoria, Ill.

Dear Miss Hollander:

In the past few years, I've read some interesting and remarkable novels. But none compares with the one you have written. I must congratulate you on your frankness and honesty. And through your eyes, I have realized that though brought up to think differently about houses of prostitution—to think of them as house of ill-fame—through your honest account I now know better, that they are really houses of pleasure. I would now rate them with such professions as nursing, teaching, social work, or a number of other socially useful pursuits.

This is not a value judgment on my part. Because of my size, I've had to limit my sex life to whore houses most of my life. Although I am over 6'5", I do weigh in the vicinity of 375 lbs, pretty big for most women. And so I have learned to appreciate beauty and honesty from ladies of the evening.

I know that we move in different circles, Xaviera, but maybe we shall have the opportunity to meet one of these days. Though I honestly doubt it. You enjoy nightclubs and fancy restaurants, while I enjoy walking in the woods in autumn, or fishing, being part of all those natural things God meant for us to enjoy. That is the sounds, the smells and even the solitude of nature.

I am sorry if I have taken up too much of your valuable time, for when I write it is how I feel and not how I would like to feel. If you can, please write.

Sincerely yours,

Harmon E. Banks

Corning, N.Y.

Dear Xaviera,
You say you don't like the title, "hooker." Would you prefer "public toilet"? It can be arranged.

Mrs. Walter (Carlotta) Yancy

Hamilton, Ohio

Dear Miss Hollander,
If ever you get back into the "interior decorating" business again please send me your card! Your book makes "Peyton Place" look like "Rebecca of Sunnybrook Farm" or "Gidget Goes to Disneyland." If you should happen to have any "friends" in the Milwaukee area, I wish you'd send me their names and numbers.

Why don't you revolutionize your profession and start a "Computer Fucking" service? You could make it on an escalating scale ($5 for messengers, $100 for bankers). In this way I feel you could provide an *essential* social service and, if you plow all the profits back into the business, register as a non-profit organization as well!

All the luck in the world, honey.

Harlan Wells

Waukegan, Wisc.

Dear Xaviera,

I loved your book, but what impressed me most about it was how much our sexual attitudes are accidental matters.

When I was 14 or 15, my father and I had a large difference of opinion about what time I should get home at night. He wanted me in at 9, while most of my friends were allowed to be out till 10 or 11, or later. Being naturally rebellious, this led to many battles. As a result he frequently locked me out for the night. This didn't bother me too much—I used to head for the nearest park, find a comfortable bench and go to sleep.

One night I was awakened by the unmistakable sound of panting and sighing and (I was just old enough to realize) sexual moaning. Not ten feet from me were a young intern and a nurse and they weren't playing doctor. They hadn't seen me and had chosen a grassy spot and were fucking with complete abandon. She was a little on the plump side, very pretty and terrifically hot natured, and I'll never forget how she looked when she came, which was more than five or six times.

Apparently, this was their regular trysting place, because I saw them fucking or sucking each other many times that summer. Oddly, perhaps because they were so wrapped up in each other, they never noticed me.

Well, this colored my whole attitude toward nurses—not to mention sex—and I could never look at one without getting a very stiff erection. I started dating nurses as soon as I was 18 or 19 and at 21 I married a plump blonde nurse who might very well have been that same hot-assed nurse I used to see getting fucked regularly.

We've been very happy together—sometimes we even make it in the park—and my father, who I hate, will never know what a favor he did me by locking me out those nights.

"Nurse lover"

Aldo T. Grimaldi
Glendale, Calif.

279

Dear Life-Spirit Xaviera!

Emma Bovary in "Madame Bovary"!

Sonya in "Crime and Punishment"!

Millie in "Of Human Bondage"!

Sadie Thompson and Nana and all the others!

And Molly Bloom, did ever a female voice sing so sweetly of the joys of love!

Lady, dear lady, do you recognize what a venerable, estimable literary tradition you have lived out!

Yours avidly for literary traditions of life/love motifs,

Leonardo Don Conversi, Candidate for Ph.D.

Dept. of Comparative Literature

Harpur College

Binghamton, N.Y.

Dear Miss Hollander,

I have just finished reading your book & I loved it. Every bit! The life you have lived! You have done everything most of us yearn to do and more. You have seen so much, done so much and you seemed to have loved it all! Even with all the sickies, wierdos and corruption you've experienced you still seem to love people and life. Too bad more of us aren't blessed with your *joie de vivre*.

I'm 19 and quite ordinary. But I've wanted something different from life for a long time but wondered what there was. Maybe you've told me.

Thanks *beaucoup*.

Love,

Miss Pamela Allentuck

Ottawa, Canada

Miss Xaviera Hollander,

Several of us in my office have read your sensational book and we all enjoyed it very much. During one of our daily lunch-time discussions, the subject of what sign under the Zodiac you were born came up. I had no idea people could get so excited about something nobody could be sure of. So would you be kind enough to clear it up and tell us what sign you were born under? You wouldn't believe it, Xaviera, but there are some people actually not speaking to each other over this issue.

Thanks in advance for helping to restore peace to what used to be a very pleasant office to work in. Also, we have some small bets laid, so your sign is of "business" concern to us as well.

Hopefully,

Elizabeth Ann Byrnes

Louisville, Ky.

Hi Xaviera,

My name is Roy—I want to tell you how much I enjoyed your book, thinking that it would be disappointing if no one would take the time to appreciate your effort. I wanted to respond. Also the manuscript was a big benefit to me. A person's technique needs constant upgrading and maintenance. Your detailed and honest approach really turned me on—as well as answering many questions that I had been curious about. Needless to say, I read some of the Chapters several times.

At any rate many of your personal accounts linger on my mind and that is exciting—relating to that kind of sweet zestful nonsense occupies a big part of man's fantasy.

With a bit of bravery, and knowing your interest in men, I would like to think of myself as an immaculently clean, extra, but not too extra, good-looking, and a strong athletic type. Only 5'10", I'm well-proportioned and quite resourseful and capable. I sometimes draw, paint, read, or play Monopoly to fill time as needed. My job presses me to display endurance, patience, and be mentally alert—as well as requiring a lot of physical strength.

Hoping you can continue in your calling

Roy D. Schoolman

Charleston, South Carolina

Howdy, Miss Hollander,

I liked your book real well.

I come hail from a town of 46 men, women and cows and it seems to me, whenever I'm joshing among the men at the country store, that your little book must be about the most interesting thing to happen to this town since old Premier Khrushchev passed through not 50 miles away. I swear to you—every plumb man in this little community has read your book! And a lot of the womenfolk, too!

Well, what I'm writing to say is that you're some kind of woman—and if you ever get out this way—HOOOE! —we sure wish you'd visit with the folks in Grover's Corners, which is, by the way, the home of the eight-finger occarino (1896).

Hope to see you,

Henry M. Isaac

Grover's Corners, Iowa

Dear Ms. Hollander,

Vanier College is a College of General and Professional Education located in suburban Montreal, and in its third

282

year of operation . . . groping, developing, searching for ways and means to better equip its students to face an ever-changing society.

As part of its smorgasbord of activities for the 1973 winter semester, Vanier is in the midst of organizing an extensive workshop/conference/festival on Sexuality (the actual title hasn't been worked out yet) for the week of March 19-23.

If you are free to speak to the Vanier Community sometime during that week, we would be greatly honoured to accommodate you at your convenience and help to facilitate any arrangements that need to be made.

It is through first-hand information that the youth of today can build towards a positive future. We sincerely hope that you will be able to spend some time with us.

Looking forward to hearing from you.

Yours sincerely,

Allan Shatzky

Social Animator
Vanier College
Montreal, Quebec

Dear Xaviera:

I've read your book "The Happy Hooker" and I was very moved by it. I wish that I could in some way contribute to the legalizing of the houses of pleasure.

Right now I'm stationed in Puerto Rico and I've been to two such places. They weren't high class places but the girls were clean and relaxing. If I should ever have the money I would like to visit a place such as yours.

With all sincerety I hope everything turns out ok for you. I know I'm only one person, but I've told my friends about your book and I know they'll feel as I do. We might not be able to do much now as most of us are only 20, but we are the future of this country. We will be deciding tomorrow's laws.

We fight and some of us die for our country. My friends and I and all the younger people have new ideas and new moral codes. I believe that some day the "houses of pleasure" will be legalized and respected business.

You are not alone in your fight. God be with you.

Peace and Love,

James Margolies

1200 6th Eng. Br.

Camp Garcia Viegus Island, P.R.

Dear Xaviera,

I need a boost to get me up to where you've been. I make a living at loving, but when it comes down to it, I'm also sentimental at times. "On the house Angie," I call myself when I've felt sorry for some guy and given it away.

I'm in my early thirties but can easily pass for 26-27. I've got a real good body and nice skin. Never had a disease. I'm a real down-to-earth person and like enjoying life in all its phases—which means I enjoy sex (either one!). I've never been a bar hustler, but I have worked the room robot route.

What I want to do is have a real nice escort service. A lot of time and effort will have gone into this if I can do it. And money. Thank God I have the political pull I'll need.

Why I'm writing, besides to tell you I loved your book, is to ask a favor: do you think I should have a separate apartment for living and another one for business? I can afford both rents, I think, but it seems kind of silly.

I know you have better things to do with your time, and

haven't thought about these problems since you got out of the business, but I really would appreciate a reply.

Yours truly,

Angela O'Keefe
Miami, Fla.

Dear Madame Hollander,

Having read your scandalous but often wrong-headed book, I have two "bones to pick with you," as you Americans are fond of saying.

I am of French extraction and proud of it. Surely even a rather poorly educated Dutch girl like you has heard of our universally accepted reputation as great lovers.

To accuse us of being deficient in "personal hygiene" is a highly subjective judgment on your part. Some men, carrying on a number of love affairs, bathe and perfume themselves daily; others—especially denizens of bagnios and bordellos—I expect do not. On the theory that they are only sleeping with "bought" women, for whom they have paid in brass. Love, you see, or its illusionary aspects —is the guiding factor.

But your most offensive remark about Frenchmen was to refer to us as "cute little lovers." This is like referring to *Tyrannosaurus Rex* as a household pet. I invite you to come to Quebec City and meet some of the "cute little lovers" among my fellow compatriots. We will send you home so well spermatized that you will desist from writing such arrant nonsense in your next book, Madame.

Etienne Saint-Servin
Quebec City, Quebec

285

Dear Miss Hollander,

I have read your book and also saw you twice on the "Lou Gordon Show." I think you are a lovely, witty and remarkable woman. I would very much like to get to know you personally.

I am a reserved, intelligent and congenial man of 41 who has led a very normal but routine life and have not had nearly any of the excitement and variety you've experienced. I have three college degrees and have taught school for 20 years, but I consider myself very socially introverted. I was married once for three years and have had several girlfriends, but most of the time I've been too shy or too insecure to try to relate to a woman with ease. I'm 5'9", 165 lbs., good build, Caucasian, clean and neat, average looking, healthy, energetic, emotionally sound, and have a good position. However, I guess I'm very lonely for someone like you. I know I've always been a loner (I was sick through most of my 20's and early 30's) but I very well know and still can't relate to the average woman.

I'm really a kind, easy-going man. I believe in God and am ethical, but I'm not religious. I don't believe in any organized church or religion. I don't live by any moral code, but try to live by the golden rule. I think you are a very honest, ethical, and yes, moral person!! I can really say that if I would have had you as a friend, I would not be lonely and my life would have been so much richer.

May I see you sometime? I am no "kook" nor do I ever write to celebrities. This is the first letter like this I've ever written. I'm not after sex or your body. I would primarily like to have a date with you should you be in southern California again. I'm free all summer, so if you will let me know where you are during the summer, I will come to see you. I'm no pest or pushy—I just would like to have a nice, normal date with you. You are very appealing to me and I'm not ashamed to say I get very excited by the pictures of you on the book.

I can supply you with a great deal of solid references. I've never been arrested, I don't use people—I will honestly never talk about knowing you. I'm no publicity-seeker because I don't like that sort of thing.

If you will write to me I will be so happy to answer any questions that you may have about me. Of course, I'd like to be able to know you as a close friend, but that might take a long time.

Perhaps you want to know why I must write such a letter as this—I could have girlfriends if I went against my convictions and played roles and games, but I can't do it—I've got to be myself—that's why I'm so shy and so lonely. Most women want to be bought like merchandise or want to manipulate by using their bodies as bait. I just want to know an honest, open, and refreshing woman who can relate to a man on all levels.

May I see you this summer? I really think we'd get along perfectly. I won't hurt you in any way—I'm a very sensitive person and would not want to harm such a beautiful person as you.

Willard W. Gosling

San Diego, Calif.

Dear Ms. Hollander:

I've read your books, and liked both of them a lot, and have something I want to say to you.

I'm only 14, true, but I was bar mitzvahed a year ago and accordingly am considered "a man" in our tradition.

And it's as a man I speak to you.

I think it's damn rotten of the U.S. Government to make you leave this country, even if you did it 'without duress." I think prostitution will eventually be legalized— for both sexes, for that matter! People's sex lives are their own fucking business, aren't they? It gets me boiling mad to think how governmental types want to pry into people's personal existences!

I hope you will be able to come back to America and

open a string of "pleasure houses" that will make McDonald's green with envy.

All success,

David Rosenthal
St. Louis, Ill.

Dear Madam:

We read your book and got a lot of fun out of doing so.

So maybe you can help us. I have a great sex life with my husband, but a few months ago I finally confessed to him that I am really a bisexual person. He was delighted. The thought of two girls in bed made him hard as a rock.

But—when we arranged it, it was another story. I made it possible for us to have another girl—a beautiful girl, as it happened—in bed with us, and everything was just wonderful—until my husband's erection went to half mast. He said he was so turned on by all the action between us that he couldn't keep it up indefinitely, but that doesn't really make sense to me. We've tried twice since then, and while the evening hasn't been an entire fiasco, it wasn't what it was supposed to be. The truth is my girl friend would have been pretty annoyed if I hadn't done her up brown myself.

Do you have any ideas about this? It's hurt our personal sex life, without my girl friend, and I'm wondering if the whole thing was such a good idea in the first place.

Sincerely,

Mrs. "Ginger" Lockhart
Huntington, W. Va.

Dear Lady Chatterly:

You asked for brainstorms. . . .

How about a television show on CITY-TV in Toronto? It would go on at noon (sorry about the early hour, but there's a reason for it) and would be a combination cooking and talk show. Like the one Dinah Shore is doing.

The first guests you'd interview would be all the people who interviewed *you* on your publicity tour.

You'd call the show "Box Lunch" (pun intended)!

After all, if Gypsy Rose Lee could do a talk show or Graham Kerr get high on a cooking show, why not you?

I've also got an idea on where to locate an "unbustable" brothel in "Fun City," but it's rather audactious.

A fan,

James Gould Lee
Detroit, Mich.

Dear Xaviera,

I am a 16 year old female and I guess you could call me a part-time prostitute. I read your first book when it first came out and really dug the shit out of it.

I'm in the hospital now, but I get out in a few days. Believe it or not, it was my English teacher who brought me a copy of "Xaviera!" I read it as though books were going out of style, and the chapter on David reminded me of something like that which happened to me a few years ago.

I also liked the questions and answers—they were really interesting and I think I learned quite a lot from them.

My ultimate goal is to meet you and if we get that far, to go to bed with you. There isn't any part of your body I wouldn't go over with "loving care." I'm sure you get a lot of letters like this, but I really mean it. I've been looking at women since I was 10 or 11 years old.

Well, I'd better sign off now because I hear the people

coming with my dinner. Take care of yourself and may God keep you safe and out of jail.

With love,

Vernice Schoonover

St. Paul, Minn.

Dear Xaviera,

I have known for years that pleasure houses, such as yours, were in existence. However, I personally have never come across one. I hardly ever get up to New York, but if I knew I wouldn't once again strike out—I'd make the trip.

I imagine what I really want is a very knowledgeable, very attractive and appealing but strong, firm hand to teach me what you taught that young 17-year-old in Puerto Rico. When you get down to brass tacks, I'm plenty green. Perhaps you could provide me with a reference in my own area.

Some of those freaky things sound exciting. Nevertheless, if I were involved, I would do whatever is necessary to avoid becoming obnoxious. Page 247 of your book handles one of the main things on my mind; page 257 takes care of the other in the second paragraph—next to last and the last sentence.

If one is absolutely certain of getting what he wants, right on the button, the whole event may be worth his time and effort. It doesn't seem like I can help myself very much. I need somebody to intercede. I hope you'll both call and write. And be explicit in detail each time. I am no trouble. And that's the gospel truth.

Sincerely yours,

Kenny Kupferman

Arlington, Va.

Dear Xaviera,

Just finished reading your second book, and was very pleased to learn from the last page that there will be a third! Just had to stop and take the time to let you know.

The spirit, and straight forwardness, of your writing style is indeed an oasis, and a delight . . . especially after having finished Irving Wallace's new book, "The Word." He writes a very good book, but compared to your recent book, and the "Happy Hooker," it is lacking. Perhaps it is due to the fact that his is fiction, and your book is not. Fiction can't out ring the truth. It has a ring of it's own.

I realize that the chance of this letter ever reaching you is very slim, but somewhere along the line it may be of interest. Thank you for your perspectives. They have presented a greater richness and joy to life . . . and awareness. And that's what life is all about.

May 1973 be a great year for you and yours.

Sincerely,

Jeffrey Shea
Eugene, Oregon

Dear Ms. Hollander,

I have read your book and found it very enjoyable reading material and better than any "dirty novel" for pornographic enjoyment. It is a shame that you haven't been on nationwide T.V. I hope I will get a chance to see you on T.V. someday.

Anyway, I have a question for you. Do you know of anyone who has made it with 2 or 3 men at once? To be specific, I mean a cock in the ass, a cock in the vagina, and a cock in the mouth all at the same time? Could this be done without too much pain or physical injury? This has been my supreme fantasy, ever since I was a girl of 11 or 12. I always imagine a big cock in my vagina, a small one up my ass (so as not to be too painful) and a medium-size

291

cock to suck on. To make it even better, if it was physically possible, would be to also have someone suck a nipple and someone to tongue my clit. That would require 4 or 5 people all at once!! I wonder if you have ever had an experience of this kind or if you would try it.

Also I think I have a unique way of masturbating which I discovered quite by accident when I was only 13. I use a shower hose with the end cut off and regulate the flow and temperature of the water until it is comfortable, and direct the pulse of water at my clitoris and it is most enjoyable and relaxing while taking a bath.

I am 23 and full of sex fantasies. I hope you can answer this in your next book because I know you are too busy to give personal replies. Besides this is quite personal and I'm living with my parents now.

Thank you,

Charlene Detwiler
Dayton, Tenn.

Dear Xaviera,

You mention in your book (which is a gas) that you love to groove on voices. It reminded me of a friend of mine, Len, who has the guts of a burglar. He's a photographer and he left his left leg in Vietnam, where we fought together. But he's as strong as a bull and he doesn't let this stop him. He's even gotten into a coupla street fights since his Nam days, and he's all right until he hits the deck. Then he's as helpless as a baby.

Anyway, never one to let an opportunity go by, he was on the phone one day, couldn't get his party and cursing like a son of a bitch he dialled the operator for help. Pretty soon he forgot about the phone call, because this operator had one of those purring, cock-teasing voices. Since there's nothing shy about Len, he laid it right in there.

"Baby," he said, in that soft phony voice he puts on

with broads he's trying to make, "listening to that great voice of yours, I just want to fuck it and eat it."

Well, wouldn't you know the lucky stiff hit pay dirt? He could tell from her attitude that she not only wasn't shocked but that the idea excited her.

They made a date for the following Tuesday to meet on the corner of 42nd and 8th Ave. in Manhattan. A big pick-up corner. Turned out that she wasn't bad looking and, of course, married, but that never stopped Len. He took her back to his pad on Cornelia St. and she was fascinated by the fact that he had only one leg.

"How's this as a substitute?" Len said, putting his stiff, fiery-red joint into her hand.

He's been balling her ever since.

Sincerely,

Jim Colangelo
Rahway, N.J.

Dear Miss Hollander,

Hi! I'm with you! Why can't Prostitution be made legal? Why is it still unlawful? Is it the men or Women who are against it?

I couldn't put your book down and I know it's true of men and their Acts of really Wanting to pay for sex because they don't feel "guilty" when they pay, and their love making is longer than when they don't pay, cause they worry about the wife finding out the Whole entire trip, true?

I lived in L.A. Cal seven years. And there are "Male hustlers" out there! And plenty of 'em too! I know plenty of "unhappy horny housewifes" who'd love for it to be made legal and lots of us singles would too!! Murder seems to be okay now doesn't it?!

If Abortions *Are* made legal then so should Prostitution!!

Housewives love to have "real love" made to them, and need extra money and love to "hustle," but here in Gary people are so square anyway, about ten years behind Calif. and 15 behind N.Y. And Consevetive as can be!

I dig breaking in male virgins myself and teaching them how to make love the right way and to relax, and not Wham—Mam—Thank you—bye! There are some who do try and do pretty good I've met, but frenching here hasn't caught on yet and that's such a shame.

Please forgive me for being so foreward.

Jolene Stebbins

Gary, Indiana

2/28/73 A.D.

Dear Xaviera:

I just got done reading your new book and it was FANTASTIC!!

I read your first book too and it was COSMIC. I hope you write me back because I told all my friends that I was writing you and it would be a bummer if you didn't.

I can't wait until your next book comes out because as sure as hell I'll buy it.

I wish you would show a picture of Larry in your next book because I would like to see him, not that I am a Faggot.

In your chapter "The Producer's Hoax," when that dude was raping you, I would have beat the shit out of him with a chair leg.

He must have been a sadist.

Ya know the idea of swallowing sperm just turns me OFF. It may be good for the skin but I'll be goddamned if I'll drink that shit.

I wish I could talk to you and you could autograph my book.

If you ever come to Bakersfield, make it known. Okay? I would like to meet you.

I'm glad you are honest about your sex life, because it takes a lot of guts to say you jacked off a German Shepherd. Wow?!

Oh, by the way I am 15 years old.

I HOPE that you will write back just once *please?*

I also hope that you use this letter in your next book. All my Friends would really flip and even more if you write me a letter. Wow!!

bye for now,

Jackie Baldwin

Bakersfield, Calif.